Computers and Quantity Surveyors

Macmillan Building and Surveying Series
Series Editor: Ivor H. Seeley
        Emeritus Professor, Trent Polytechnic
Advanced Building Measurement, second edition, Ivor H. Seeley
An Introduction to Building Services Christopher A. Howard
Applied Valuation Diane Butler
Asset Valuation Michael Rayner
Building Economics, third edition Ivor H. Seeley
Building Maintenance, second edition Ivor H. Seeley
Building Quantities Explained, fourth edition Ivor H. Seeley
Building Surveys, Reports and Dilapidations Ivor H. Seeley
Building Technology, third edition Ivor H. Seeley
Civil Engineering Contract Administration and Control Ivor H. Seeley
Civil Engineering Quantities, fourth edition Ivor H. Seeley
Civil Engineering Specification, second edition Ivor H. Seeley
Computers and Quantity Surveyors A. J. Smith
Contract Planning and Contract Procedures B. Cooke
Contract Planning Case Studies B. Cooke
Environmental Science in Building, second edition R. McMullan
Introduction to Valuation D. Richmond
Principals of Property Investment and Pricing W. D. Fraser
Quantity Surveying Practice Ivor H. Seeley
Structural Detailing P. Newton
Urban Land Economics and Public Policy, fourth edition P. N. Balchin, J. L. Kieve and G. H. Bull
1980 JCT Standard Form of Building Contract, second edition R. F. Fellows

Series Standing Order

If you would like to receive future titles in this series as they are published, you can make use of our standing order facility. To place a standing order please contact your bookseller or, in case of difficulty, write to us at the address below with your name and address and the name of the series. Please state with which title you wish to begin your standing order. (If you live outside the United Kingdom we may not have the rights for your area, in which case we will forward your order to the publisher concerned.)

Customer Services Department, Macmillan Distribution Ltd
Houndmills, Basingstoke, Hampshire, RG21 2XS, England.

Computers and Quantity Surveyors

A. J. Smith

Department of Surveying
Trent Polytechnic, Nottingham

MACMILLAN

First published 1989

Published by
MACMILLAN EDUCATION LTD
Houndmills, Basingstoke, Hampshire RG21 2XS
and London
Companies and representatives
throughout the world

Laserset by
Ponting–Green Publishing Services, London

Printed and bound in Great Britain at
The Camelot Press plc, Southampton

British Library Cataloguing in Publication Data

Smith A. J.
    Computers and Quantity Surveyors
    1. Great Britain. Quantity surveying.
    Applications of micro computer systems
    I. Title.
    624.1'042'0285416

    ISBN 0–333–49161–0 Pbk
    ————

Cover photograph of a digitiser kindly supplied by Techsonix (U.K.) Ltd.

For Christine, Joanna and Elaine

Contents

It is difficult not to believe that the computer will become the medium through which increasingly large parts of design and construction will be done in the future; taking over from the manual process just as inexorably as steam power and machines took over from manual labour in the industrial revolution.

John Chalmers
'Computing for construction in the 'eighties'
Chartered Quantity Surveyor May 1979

Preface

The quantity surveyor and the computer have been partners in an intense love–hate relationship for over 30 years; indeed, it would be difficult to find any other profession in which the relationship between man and machine has generated, by turns, so much discussion; hope and optimism; disappointment and disillusion. Even now the rank and file of the profession is still sharply divided between those who claim 'computer literacy' and who consequently venerate the computer and all its works and those who, with apparently equal pride, proclaim themselves to be 'techno-peasants'.

It is not the intention of this book to attempt to persuade students or fellow practitioners to follow either view. The intention is to attempt to inform rather than to influence; to try to blow away some of the mystique which still surrounds the use of computer systems in order that, no matter which side of the computing fence one eventually elects to stand, at least the decision is made on some rational basis.

This book is therefore divided into two parts, the first part (chapters 1 to 8) dealing with general concepts of information technology, and the latter part (chapters 9 to 12) dealing with specific quantity surveying issues. In many ways this division is, of course, artificial as indeed is the subdivision in part 2 between the various aspects of quantity surveying, and the notion that the quantity surveyor stands alone from the rest of the construction team. I also recognise that there are some areas of work in which quantity surveyors are employed which are not specifically considered here; nonetheless, the first part of the book should still provide a useful introduction to the technology.

The book is directed primarily towards providing students with a basic grounding in the use of computers by quantity surveyors. It covers a wide range of subjects, and I am only too aware that some areas are treated in a very superficial way; this is partly deliberate and partly imposed by pressures of space, but I hope that the references given will aid the research of those wishing to pursue particular aspects of the subject to a greater depth. I hope that the book may also be of interest to those quantity surveying practitioners who have yet to come to terms with the technology, and also to students and practitioners of other construction disciplines.

A.J. Smith

Acknowledgements

I am indebted to Brian George, Senior Lecturer in the Department of Building and Environmental Health, Trent Polytechnic for permission to use extracts from his paper 'Project management and micro computers', first delivered at the 'Quantity Surveyors and Computers' conference held at the Barbican in April 1988, in the preparation of chapter 13, and for his most helpful comments on the draft.

I am also most grateful to Rob Bradgate of the Department of Legal Studies, Trent Polytechnic for his advice on the legal issues discussed in chapter 4.

May I also freely acknowledge with much gratitude all of the help and co-operation given by the many friends and colleagues too numerous to mention with whom I have discussed ideas and argued principles over the past twenty years; many of the ideas we discussed have found their way in one form or another into this book. In particular, thanks are due to my colleagues from whom I have learned a great deal, especially Dick Massey, Phil Hawkins, Graham Williams and Dave Rowe at Trent Polytechnic, Vernon Foster and Ivor Neal of Derbyshire County Council and Wally Harlow, former Chief Quantity Surveyor at Derbyshire County Council.

Thanks are also due to Professor Ivor Seeley for his most helpful comments and to Jaqui Hunt for the illustrations.

Finally my grateful thanks to my family for all of the tolerance, help and encouragement given whilst this book was in preparation.

General Concepts

1 The Quantity Surveyor and the Computer – a Short History

Objectives

At the end of this chapter you should be able to:

- Outline the history of commercial data processing.
- Outline the major developments which have taken place in the use of computers by quantity surveyors during the past 25 years.
- Outline the ways in which quantity surveyors are most likely to use computers today.

Early developments in computing and data processing

The first consideration when discussing the development of early computer systems is to decide exactly where to begin. Most histories of computing, for example Evans (1981), begin with the development of mechanical counting machines by people such as Pascal and Babbage, but whilst these machines have much to do with the use of computing 'engines' to solve mathematical problems they have little or nothing to do with either the development of electronic computers or the use of such machines to process data.

The first electronic, as opposed to electro-mechanical, computers are now generally acknowledged to have been the 'Colossus' machines first described in Michie (1973), which were built by the Post Office Research Station for the Department of Communications of the British Foreign Office, the first of which was delivered to the Government Code and Cypher School, Bletchley Park in December 1943. A fuller account of Colossus following the release of further information by the Ministry of Defence in 1975 is given in Randell (1980).

Most of the developments in computers at this time were, of course, highly secret and it was not until after the end of the Second World War that the use of computers for commercial data processing was considered. Considerable use had however been made of the electro-mechanical punched card sorting equipment, developed around the turn of the century by Hollerith and his contemporaries, for accounting, processing of census data and the like. By the end of the second world war the use of such machines was commonplace and companies such as IBM were already well established in the data processing field. The origins of data processing can therefore be said to pre-date the development of the electronic computer by almost half a century.

It was then against this background of data processing experience and in the spirit of new optimism just after the war that J. Lyons & Co. began, in 1947, to investigate the use of computers for commercial data processing and eventually, in consultation with computer specialists from the computing laboratory at Cambridge University, installed LEO, the Lyons Electronic Office. LEO finally became operational towards the end of 1953, although Lavington (1980:p. 35) points out that LEO was really a re-engineered version of the EDSAC (Electronic Delay Storage Automatic Calculator) originally developed in Cambridge in 1949.

Although LEO was the first computer in the world to be used for commercial data processing, Lavington (1980:p. 41) claims that the world's first commercially available computer was the Ferranti Mk.1 based on the Manchester Automatic Digital Machine (MADM) developed at Manchester University, the first of which was delivered in February 1951. Evans (1980:p. 92) however claims that the first commercially successful computer was the UNIVAC 1 the first of which was delivered in March 1951.

It should be pointed out that by no means everyone viewed the future of the computer with the optimism shown by Lyons. Fisher, McKie and Mancke (1983:p. 14) quote Cuthbert Hurd, then IBM Head of Applied Science, as stating that he was told, in 1949, by IBM president Thomas Watson Snr. that the single IBM Selective Sequence Electronic Calculator then in existence could solve all of the important scientific problems in the world requiring calculation. Hurd is also reported as saying that a substantial body of opinion within IBM at the time:

> ...could not imagine that enough problems or applications could ever be proposed by IBM's potential customers to keep a computer busy because such machines were to have the capability of processing several thousand operations per second.

The quantity surveyor and data processing

In the beginning...

The origins of the quantity surveyor's love–hate relationship with computing can be traced back to the mid 1950s, when an article, Stafford (1957), was published in *The Builder* magazine. In the article the author, a practising quantity surveyor, advocated the use of punched card sorting equipment for the abstracting stage of the bill production process. The true origins may in fact be even earlier, since Nott (1967) claims that discussions began in the Architects Department of Hertfordshire County Council as early as 1955/56.

Stafford's ideas appear to have been first put into practice by quantity surveyors in the CLASP group attached to Nottinghamshire County Council working in conjunction with Derby and Coventry City Councils, and the first successful implementation of a punched card sorting system for this kind of work was reported in *The Builder* in August 1958 (Cooke (1958)). Eighteen months later, in March 1960, Braine and Pritchard (1960) described another system, again using punched card sorting equipment, this time developed within the Quantity Surveying Division of the War Office. It is interesting to note that the publication of Braine and Pritchard's article provoked a rather acerbic response from the respected quantity surveyor and author A.J. Willis, Willis (1960), who questioned whether the reporting of such fringe activities was not a waste of valuable magazine space.

Willis's reservations were not however shared by all, and it was later reported in the Chartered Surveyor (RICS (1961a)) that:

> In September 1959 the Quantity Surveyors Committee endorsed the appointment of a Working Party to consider and report on the possible place of computers in quantity surveying practice. A further Working Party was formed in February 1960 to deal with one facet of this investigation namely 'to look into the possibilities of the use of computers in connection with the working up of quantity surveyors dimensions' and to report to the main working party.

The final report of this latter working party, RICS (1961b), was presented at a quantity surveyors general meeting held on the 18th October 1961, and the ideas presented, together with the views expressed in the interim report, RICS (1961a), had a profound influence on the development of computer systems for quantity surveyors for the following twenty years.

Among the main themes were:

i) Bill production by computer was not only possible but relatively easy:

> There are unlikely to be any insuperable problems to the use of computers for the working up of quantity surveyors' dimensions for the general run of building and civil engineering work
>
> (RICS (1961a))

ii) an industry-wide coded standard library of descriptions was essential:

> Standard descriptions are inevitable...Standardisation of descriptions...would, we feel, help the industry to build more cheaply
>
> (RICS (1961a))

> We therefore recommend that the RICS should...consider the production of a standard coded library...
>
> (RICS (1961b))

iii) one result of the use of computers would probably be a co-ordinated approach to project information and planning:

> The building and civil engineering industries...are being urged, and are themselves striving to improve their planning and construction methods...the adoption by the quantity surveying profession of data-processing techniques might well be the catalyst for speeding up the desired changes.
>
> (RICS (1961b))

iv) the re-use of the quantity surveyor's data by the contractor was seen as a good idea:

> Using the data which produced the bill of quantities to provide data for:
>
> 1) planning constructional operations
> 2) ordering materials
> 3) forecasting labour requirements
> 4) bonusing
>
> (RICS (1961b))

v) computer processing of bills of quantity was to reduce the cost of building:

> We forsee the adoption of integrated data processing techniques speeding construction and lowering costs.
>
> (RICS (1961b))

With hindsight one could perhaps query the validity of all of the above. So far as the first was concerned development of a comprehensive, working and marketable system as opposed to a test or demonstration system proved, for most developers, to be anything but easy. As an example consider the system developed by the Development Group of Chartered Quantity Surveyors, a consortium formed of twelve of the leading quantity surveying practices in the United Kingdom, who began work on a billing system before mid 1966 (see RICS (1967a)) with the intention of having a system operational by the end of that year. RICS (1967a) however admits that anticipated completion of a basic system would be delayed by about a year, and the complete system would not be ready before 1968. By November 1972 an acceptable commercial system was still not generally available, and general release was not anticipated until mid 1973. (Development Group of Chartered Quantity Surveyors (1972)). Whilst part of the delay can undoubtedly be attributed to the metrication of the Standard Method of Measurement in 1968, it is clear that the early programs were not satisfactory and that the difficulties of development were severely underestimated.

It could also be argued that the preoccupation with coding of the data has restricted rather than advanced the march of progress. The impact of coding was airily dismissed in the initial reports, RICS (1961b) for example said:

> In the course of time however...the taker-off may write just brief descriptions plus the code number. Coding may then actually speed up taking off rather than delay it.

Dent (1964:p99) went even further:

> Once it is decided that a modification of existing taking off procedure is acceptable then the obvious person to do the coding is the taker-off himself. The pattern which will eventually emerge is probably one in which conventional descriptions disappear altogether from the dimensions, and codes will take their place.

There is little doubt that the readiness of those quantity surveyors involved in systems development to accept the necessity of coding, and their occasionally ingenious attempts to find economic ways to do it, allowed this archaic, error prone, boring and unpopular chore to be tolerated in quantity surveying systems long after alternative techniques became available.

The hope that the adoption of data processing techniques by the quantity surveyor would lead to better co-ordinated project documentation and planning might have appeared to be convincing at the time in the light of contemporary developments in information science, but in the cold light of day it is difficult to believe that quantity surveyors seriously expected the architectural and engineering professions to change their ways simply because the quantity surveyor wanted to use a computer.

Perhaps the true reason why so much time, money and effort was expended on billing systems is none of the altruistic ones given in the working party reports. Perhaps the true and overriding reason is set out in the first few paragraphs of RICS (1961a) and is rather more selfish:

> During the past 15 years these traditional methods (of bill production) have, however, suffered for the following reasons:
>
> (1) the raised status of the quantity surveying profession has attracted entrants who, in the main, aspire to taking off as quickly as possible and who are not content to treat working up as a career. This has created a chronic staff shortage of workers up and
>
> (2) the high levels of salaries payable to juniors by reason of full employment and the competition from industry and commerce for their services.

Quantity surveyors find that the above factors cause working up to absorb an inordinate proportion of fees.

1960–1980 – Triumph or disaster?

Following the publication of the RICS working party reports in 1961, a number of practices and organisations began work on the development of billing systems and the technical journals of the 1960s were filled with articles describing the development of one new system after another. In 1967 the RICS hosted a conference on computer techniques, and by this time the aim of the RICS Computer Applications Steering Committee had become much narrower than the brief given to the original 1959 group. It was now expressed as:

> ...to encourage the development of systems which by the use of the computer are able to produce quickly and economically Bills of Quantities to a national standard...
>
> (RICS (1967b):Foreword)

The conference brought together most of the pioneers of computerised working up and the publication of the papers presented, RICS (1967b), which includes a verbatim transcript of the discussions and an excellent bibliography, provides a comprehensive survey of the computer techniques in use at the time. Overall the tone is one of optimism although Fletcher (1967) sounds somewhat disappointed with progress when he says, of the profession's response to the 1961 report:

> The profession generally remains largely uninterested and gave no encouragement to their executive; but several groups of surveyors continued their isolated efforts and others, inspired by the working party report, began exploratory work of their own. However, the essential spark of unity was lost and inevitably the developments in this field followed divergent paths, as a consequence of which none has attained, or even promises to attain, the national significance that might well have been achieved by corporate effort.

Some guide to the general degree of interest in the subject at the time of the 1967 conference can be gained from an analysis of the conference delegates, divided by types of employment:

Local authority	74
Central government	15
Private practice	35
Computer manufacturers	3
Others (institutions etc.)	11
	——
	138
	——

Extracted from RICS (1967b):appendix C

Of the 138 delegates present at the conference over half (53.62 per cent) came from local authorities and almost two thirds (64.49 per cent) from either local or central government. Only fractionally over one quarter of the delegates (25.36 per cent) came from private practice representing 22 firms. Delegates were also asked to complete a questionnaire, part of which was concerned with their use of computer systems. Of the 45 completed questionnaires listed only 20 reported that systems were actually in use (RICS(1967b):appendix A). This high level of central and local government dominance is to some extent confirmed by a collection of case studies of Bills of Quantities systems published in 1969 by the Ministry of Public Buildings and Works (MPBW (1969)); of the 16 case studies included 10 were of systems developed in either local or central government.

In 1973 the RICS again hosted a series of three conferences on computer techniques, the first of which, on 9th January, dealt with billing systems. Although many of the systems presented at that conference were simply updates of those shown in 1967, Smart (1973) felt able to comment:

> These years since 1961 have seen a growing awareness and acceptance of computer techniques throughout the profession...

Despite this optimism however a survey by the National Consultative Committee of the Building and Civil Engineering Industries conducted some five years later, NJCC (1978:p. 17), reported that:

> Despite the lead given by the RICS in 1960, the adoption of these systems has been slow.

and later (at long, long last!):

> It is possible that the original enthusiasm for 'integrated systems' obscured the significant benefits which can flow from more limited applications. We consider the potential benefits are such that research and development should be initiated to provide improved computer aids for other aspects of the quantity surveyor's role...

How then should this period be judged? Had the quantity surveying profession as a whole really begun to enthusiastically embrace automated techniques as claimed by Smart, or was the profession in general still as uninterested and ambivalent as Fletcher (1967) had imagined and NJCC (1978) appeared to confirm?

On the one hand it can clearly be seen that a few very successful systems were developed. The ideas first proposed in Monk and Dunstone (1965) for example which were later marketed by Oldacres Computers Ltd. have clearly stood the test of time, and the system marketed until the end of the 1970s by LAMSAC, which was itself based on earlier work by Hertfordshire County Council and CLASP (described in Harlow, Chapman and Swanston (1972)) was very successful and achieved widespread use, being installed in some 60 organisations worldwide. Of the other systems the MPBW 'Enviro' system, first described in Crisp (1967), was a brave attempt to eliminate the separate coding process and the Development Group system mentioned earlier, although never truly successful, embodied at least the philosophy of automatic generation of some quantities from 'key' information thus attempting to influence the taking off process.

On the other hand, however, it appears that, apart from a few large practices mainly based in London, the lack of easy access to computers restricted the main thrust of development to local and central government organisations. This process was fuelled as much by the twin enthusiasms of a fledgeling computer industry eager to sell its wares and local authority treasurers who were eager to buy them, as it was by the well thought out plans of quantity surveyors. Looking back on events then it does seem that in many authorities the computer was used because it was there; to take advantage of spare time; to ensure full usage of a very expensive piece of equipment. Of course once the machine was used to full capacity the treasurer had a very good argument for expanding the facilities to cope with the inevitable peaks which result from the full utilisation of any resource. The entire process then becomes a spiral, and the true cost of using the system for any particular task becomes impossible to calculate and often irrelevant.

So far as the computers themselves were concerned the machinery available had evolved from devices such as the Elliot 803B, which had 4K of main storage, four tape decks and paper tape input and output as used by Northamptonshire County Council in 1967 (see RICS (1967b):appendix A), to machines like the IBM 370/3031 in use in Derbyshire County Council in 1980, which had 3000K of main storage and 9518MB of disk backing storage serving 56 video display terminals, described in Widdeson (1980). Despite the dramatic increase in available computer power however the basic techniques used by quantity surveyors to solve their problems had, with the addition of a few relatively minor enhancements, remained virtually unchanged since the early 1960s. Truly innovative research and development had effectively come to an end by the mid 1960s and was not to re-emerge until the advent of the microcomputer at the end of the 1970s.

Revolution! The introduction of the microcomputer

Although the principles underlying the development of the modern micro-computer were first discovered during the early 1970s, it was not until the later years of the decade that working systems became available to the general public in the United Kingdom. When the equipment did begin to appear however it was launched with an intensive advertising campaign designed to show how friendly the new machines were, even the names were chosen with the greatest care, 'Apple' and 'PET' for example. The publicity was very effective and soon microcomputers were tipped to become the biggest growth area of the century. Trimmer (1979) was able to report:

> The resurgence of interest in computing continues. The one day seminar run by the QS (research and development) committee at the institution on the 28th. March was a sell-out...

and in a paper presented at that seminar Chalmers (1979) said:

> It is difficult not to believe that the computer will become the medium through which increasingly large parts of design and construction will be done in the future; taking over from the manual process just as inexorably as steam power and machines took over from manual labour in the industrial revolution.

The resurgence of interest reported by Trimmer is reflected in a number of events organised by the RICS and others, all concerned with the new low cost approach to computing. Unfortunately, although the computers were readily available, reliable advice from the suppliers was, in general, lacking, and exasperation with a network of computer distributors who seemed to know nothing of the possibilities of the computer they were trying to sell, beyond standard accounting and word processing packages, led to demands for unbiased advice from quantity surveyors eager to learn about the new technology. Organisations such as the Construction Industry Computing Association (CICA) provided (and still do provide) a valuable service. It is however conceivable that the new enthusiasm did not extend to actually buying any equipment; Millen wrote, in 1978:

Quantity surveyors, as any word processor salesman will tell you in an honest moment, have not been the most successful customers of the new 'space age' generation of office equipment. In fact, as far as concrete sales are concerned, they have been a relative failure.

(Millen (1978))

Whatever the true picture, in response to the quantity surveyors' pleas, the RICS, in 1981, commissioned CICA firstly to undertake a study of the use of microcomputers in the profession, and secondly to prepare a handbook which would act both as a guide to the implementation of microcomputers and would also highlight some of the pitfalls into which the unprepared could fall. The completed work, CICA (1981), was published in 1981, and much of the contents are still valid. This publication was revolutionary in that, for the very first time in a 'text book' about computing for surveyors, the authors concentrated on the quantity surveyor as a user and manager of the machine rather than attempting to teach computing. Whilst other commentators (e.g. Dent (1964), Alvey (1976) and Brandon and Moore (1983)) wrote volumes about how computers worked and how to program them, CICA (1981) relegated a brief description of their workings to an appendix and stated, quite firmly, that relying on quantity surveyors themselves to program operational systems was not, generally speaking, a good idea (CICA (1981):p. 16).

The same period began to see developments in the use of the computer for other quantity surveying activities. Links between bill production systems and computer aided design systems were perceived to be an important area, and systems are described in Daniel (1979) and Hawkins and Davidson (1979). It is however evident that the pace of development in this direction was painfully slow, and it was not until 1987 that the profession as a whole made an effort to confront the issue, when the RICS commissioned Reading University to undertake a study of computer aided design systems and the quantity surveyor. The results of the study have been published as RICS (1987). In an article describing the research Edgill and Atkin (1987) write:

Before the project commenced in earnest it was evident that many misconceptions were held by QS's. Whatever those amounted to it was clear that CAD was not well understood.

The use of computers in other areas however has apparently proceeded apace. In the post contract field the introduction of the NEDO formula for calculation of increased costs provided a fertile area for development and many practices developed their own programs. Some were made available for wider use and a typical example is described in Howard (1979), although many practitioners have since accomplished the same thing using a spreadsheet rather than by writing programs. Much interest has also been expressed in the use of computers for cost modelling, and the 'state of the art' in this area was explored at a conference held at Salford University in 1987. The papers presented, published in Brandon (1987), reveal the enormously wide range of research and development in this field.

In the area of bill production, although some of the old mainframe packages still remain, converted of course to run on microcomputers, the era of the micro has seen major developments. Hunt (1982) and Hunt (1983) for example both review systems using digitisers for measurement, whilst Hunt (1984a) reviews a revolutionary bill production package the operation of which implies fundamental changes to traditional measurement techniques. The use of computers to access and process data from remote data bases has become commonplace, and the BCIS On-line service described in Robertson (1983) is now well established.

In the realm of research the profession has once again provided a lead to the industry by securing the only construction industry project to be funded from the Government's Alvey programme of research into fifth generation computer systems. The project, which is concerned with the use of knowledge based 'expert' computer systems in quantity surveying is described in Brown (1987), and further consideration of expert systems is included in chapter 8.

How then can we sum up the reaction of the quantity surveying profession to the use of computers in the age of the micro? On the one hand it is obvious from the foregoing that some practitioners have made enormous strides in exploiting the power of the machine. On the other hand it would appear that, after almost 30 years, by no means all quantity surveyors are convinced of the benefits of computerisation, although one must admit that it has proved very difficult to establish just what the level of usage really is. Hunt (1984b) reports that the number of quantity surveying firms using computers rose from between 3 and 5 per cent in 1982 to 36 per cent by the spring of 1984; a year later the figure was quoted at 50 per cent (Hunt (1985)), and by the summer of 1986 useage was reported to be 'well in excess of 50 per cent and increasing daily' (Hunt(1986)). Lowe (1986) also quotes a figure of 'circa 50 per cent', although he goes on to say that 'many practitioners remain hostile to computerisation'. Lowe also believes that increased computer literacy from the new generation of surveyors is essential for the profession to prosper. All of this seems, at first sight, to point to a profession in which, although there may still be a few doubters, at least a majority have come to terms with the machine and yet, in late 1987, Hunt writes:

When I was asked recently how quantity surveyors had progressed in the use of computers over the past decade or so, I was tempted to say 'very little' but that would not be quite true neither would it be the whole story. The acid test of course is determined by the proportion of the profession actually using computers effectively and my current guestimate is about 10-15 per cent. There are various figures produced by the RICS and CICA ranging up to 50 per cent computer useage, but these figures relate to the number of people who '...have access to a computer...' rather then those that actually use a computer for more than ten minutes each day. The percentage also changes dramatically if word processing is not included.

(Hunt (1987))

It also appears that this malaise is not restricted to the quantity surveyor but is industry wide. Barton (1987) asks whether the whole construction industry is still illiterate and ambivalent as far as computers are concerned.

So what is the real truth? Is it necessary, as the proponents of the computer have contended for 30 years, that the quantity surveyor should take the technology on board if he is to survive? Will the use of intelligent computer aided design systems by architects and designers offer a great opportunity for the quantity surveyor to transcend the routine work which presently supports a large proportion of the profession, or will it simply make the quantity surveyor as unnecessary as the typewriter made the scribe? Will the effect of the current expert systems research be to enhance and enrich the quantity surveyor's role by making the expert's knowledge more widely available throughout the profession, thus improving the quality of the service the individual practitioner can provide to his client; or will the ready availability of such systems outside the profession result in the quantity surveyor shooting himself in the foot with the press of a computer key?

Time, of course, alone will tell, but history shows that on this issue the pundits have been more often wrong than right!

References

Alvey R.J. (1976) *Computers in quantity surveying* Macmillan

Barton P. (1987) 'Computers, construction and apathy' *Construction Computing* Winter 1987 p. 40

Braine D.G. and Pritchard D.G. (1960) 'Billing mechanised' *The Builder* 18.3.60 pp. 567–573

Brandon P.S. (ed.) (1987) *Building cost modelling and computers* E.&F.N. Spon

Brandon P.S. and Moore R.G. (1983) *Micro computers in building appraisal* Granada

Brown G. (1987) 'RICS/Alvey expert systems research' *Chartered Quantity Surveyor* April 1987 pp. 15–16

Chalmers J. (1979) 'Computing for construction in the 'eighties' *Chartered Quantity Surveyor* May 1979 pp. 131–133

CICA (1981) *Chartered quantity surveyors and the microcomputer* RICS

Cooke J.E. (1958) 'Unit quantities and the architect' *The Builder* 22.8.58 pp. 298–299

Crisp P. (1967) 'MPBW computer system for the production of Bills of Quantities' *Computer Techniques* RICS

Daniel P. (1979) 'Bills of quantity in a multi-disciplined design system' *Chartered Quantity Surveyor* May 1979 pp. 141–142

Dent C. (1964) *Quantity surveying by computer* Oxford University Press

Development Group of Chartered Quantity Surveyors (1972) *The D.G. System* paper presented to the RICS conference on billing systems held 9.1.73

Edgill B. and Atkin B. 'CAD opportunities for the Q.S.' *Chartered Quantity Surveyor* May 1987 pp. 9–10

Evans C. (1981) *The making of the micro* Victor Gollancz

Fisher F.M., McKie J.W and Mancke R.B. (1983) *IBM and the United States data processing industry, an economic history* Praeger Scientific

Fletcher L. (1967) 'Keystone of construction industry data co-ordination' *Computer techniques* RICS pp. 7–14

Harlow W.R., Chapman J.C. and Swanston R. (1972) *LAMSAC Computer System* paper presented to the RICS conference on billing systems held 9.1.73

Hawkins M. and Davidson J. (1979) 'Computer aids bills of quantities' *Chartered Quantity Surveyor* April 1979 pp. 99–105

Howard R. (1979) 'Formula price adjustment of building contracts: why use computers?' *Chartered Quantity Surveyor* April 1979 pp. 105–106

Hunt G. (1982) 'Micronotes: measure for measure' *Chartered Quantity Surveyor* January 1982 p. 161

Hunt G. (1983) 'Micronotes: innovation in digitised measurement' *Chartered Quantity Surveyor* December 1983 p. 187

Hunt G. (1984a) 'Micronotes: now you can measure your modules' *Chartered Quantity Surveyor* January 1984 p. 219

Hunt G. (1984b) 'Micronotes: micros: new developments' *Chartered Quantity Surveyor* April 1984 p.333

Hunt G. (1985) 'Micronotes: taking stock' *Chartered Quantity Surveyor* May 1985 p.381

Hunt G. (1986) 'Micronotes: quo vadis computers?' *Chartered Quantity Surveyor* June 1986 p. 13

Hunt G. (1987) 'Micronotes: making progress' *Chartered Quantity Surveyor* November 1987 p. 13

Lavington S. (1980) *Early British computers* Manchester University Press

Lowe J. (1986) 'Problems of pre-conception' *Chartered Quantity Surveyor* October 1986 p. 21

Michie D. (1973) 'The Bletchley machines' *The origins of digital computers: selected papers* Randell B. (ed) Springer-Verlag

Millen D. (1978) 'What in the world is a word processor?' *Q.S. Weekly* 30.11.78 pp. 6–7

Monk K.W. and Dunstone P.H. (1965) 'Significant development in the techniques of quantity surveying by computer' *Chartered Surveyor* February 1965 pp. 420–427

MPBW (1969) *The preparation of Bills of Quantity with the aid of computers* Ministry of Public Building and Works Directorate of Research and Information

NJCC (1978) *Computing and communication in the construction industry* Department of the Environment

Nott C.M. (1967) 'Hertfordshire County Council computerised quantity surveying services' *Computer Techniques* RICS

Randell B. (1980) 'The Colossus' *A history of computing in the twentieth century* Metropolis N., Howlett H.J. and Rota G. (eds.) Academic Press

RICS (1961a) 'The use of computers for working up' *Chartered Surveyor* April 1961 pp. 561–563

RICS (1961b) 'The use of computers for working up' *Chartered Surveyor* November 1961 pp. 248–251

RICS (1967a) 'The computer and the Bill of Quantities – towards a new era? *Chartered Surveyor* July 1967 pp. 13–17

RICS (1967b) *Computer Techniques* RICS

RICS (1987) *CAD techniques: opportunities for chartered quantity surveyors* RICS

Robertson D. (1983) 'A new cost data bank' *Chartered Quantity Surveyor* July 1983 p. 461

Smart D. (1973) *Computer aided billing systems – an evaluation* paper presented to the RICS conference on billing systems held 9.1.73

Stafford H.J. (1957) 'The standard draft bill of quantities' *The Builder* 11.1.57 p. 94

Trimmer A. (1979) 'Quantifying' *Chartered Quantity Surveyor* May 1979 p. 130

Widdeson P. (1980) *Computers in public authorities* privately published

Willis A.J. (1960) Letter to the Editor *The Builder* 25.3.60 p. 590

2 Computer Hardware

Objectives

At the end of this chapter you should be able to:

- Explain the terms 'hardware', 'software' and 'firmware'.
- Identify and describe the purpose of the main functional components of a simple office computer system.
- Discriminate between micro, mini and mainframe computers and identify their salient characteristics.
- Explain the meaning of the terms 'batch processing', 'interactive processing' and 'distributed processing'.
- Identify the main types of input and output device commonly used in quantity surveying, architecture and construction.
- Explain the meaning of some of the more commonly quoted measures of computer performance.
- Discuss the major types of backing storage device in common use.
- Outline the main factors affecting communication between computers.

Definition of some basic terms

Computer hardware is the term used to describe the actual computer machinery itself including all of the attendant peripheral devices such as keyboards, printers, screens, disk drives etc. It therefore pertains to the computer machinery as opposed to software, which is the term used to describe the programs which tell the machinery what to do. It follows then that the software is intangible, the only physical manifestation of software being the medium upon which it is stored, for example, a floppy disk or a cartridge of magnetic tape.

All modern computers are based on what has become colloquially known as 'chip' technology, a method of micro-miniaturisation which uses photo-engraving techniques to create complex integrated electronic circuits, each consisting of many different components, 'printed' onto tiny slices of some suitable material, usually silicon, called 'chips'. It is the development of this and similar high technology processes, largely fuelled by projects such as the American space programme, which has led directly to the wide range of cheap and very powerful computing equipment now available.

In the main, computer programs are stored on some type of magnetic medium, for example a disk or tape, and are 'read' into the computer's memory when required. Once the machine is switched off, however, the contents of the memory are normally lost and the program must be reloaded from the disk or tape the next time it is required. Some machines use special chips which can be programmed by a manufacturer or a system supplier in such a way that the stored program remains intact when the power is turned off, thus obviating the need to load the program from tape or disk each time the system is to be used. An example of such a chip might be that used to control an automatic washing machine. Chips such as these are therefore part hardware, the chip itself, and part software, the stored program, and are usually termed 'firmware'. Programmable chips may take a number of forms, those which have the software permanently written to them by the manufacturer are often referred to as 'read only memory' (ROM), whilst those which are supplied unprogrammed by the manufacturer and are subsequently programmed by a system supplier are referred to as 'programmable read only memory' (PROM). A special class of PROM which can be programmed, subsequently erased, usually by means of intense ultra-violet light, and re-programmed is known as 'eraseable programmable read only memory' (EPROM). The capacity of ROM type chips is usually limited and programs are usually restricted to either simple sequential routines, such as those used in an automatic washer or a computer controlling some kind of repetitive process plant, or to contain 'start-up' instructions which then themselves initiate the process of loading larger programs from disk or tape. This latter type of routine is known as a 'bootstrap loader'.

Computer 'generations'

Brandon and Moore (1983:p5) classify modern microcomputers as sixth generation machines, but the more usually accepted classification, stemming from Japanese initiatives announced in 1981, (see for example Feigenbaum and McCorduck (1983)), would classify such machines as fourth generation computers. The usually accepted definition of computer generations is as shown in table 2.1.

Some indication of the speed and complexity of computer development over the first 40 years can be gained from table 2.2, which compares ENIAC, a first generation machine with a modern 'lap-top' portable.

Table 2.1 Computer generations

Generation	Technology	Comments
1st (1940–52)	Vacuum tubes (valves)	Large, expensive, unreliable, slow
2nd (1952–64)	Transistors	Smaller, faster, needed air conditioning, maintenance reduced but still a problem
3rd (1964–71)	Integrated circuits	Smaller still, lower power consumption, more reliable, cheaper, faster
4th (1971–)	Large-scale integrated circuits	No air conditioning, cheap, fast, easy to use
5th (late 1980s/early 1990s)		Currently under development

Table 2.2 Comparison of ENIAC with DG/1 lap-top portable

Features	ENIAC (1945)	Data General DG/1 (1985)
No. of components	>100,000 valves, resistors etc.	<100 chips
Size	Approx. 100 ft × 10 ft × 3 ft	2.8 × 11.7 × 13.7 in
Weight	Approx. 100 tons	12 lb
Power consumption	140 KW	240 V or rechargeable battery
Main memory	1 K bits	512 K bytes
Backing storage	None	Two 3.5 in. disks max. 715 K

Functional components of a computer system

Having defined in very broad terms what is meant by computer hardware, let us now consider the main functional blocks which make up a computer system. All modern computer systems from the smallest micro to the largest mainframe consist of the same four essential types of equipment; namely some form of input device to allow the user(s) to communicate with the machine, some form of output device to allow the computer to communicate with the user(s), a calculation and control unit (the computer itself, sometimes referred to as the central processing unit or CPU), and some form of storage device to permit long-term storage of data and programs in machine readable form when the machine is switched off (often called 'backing storage'). The logical arrangement of the units for a simple small business system is shown in figure 2.1.

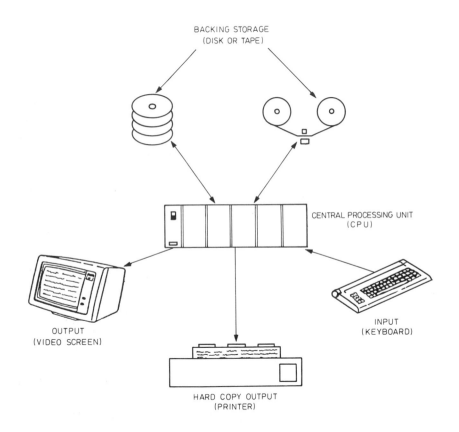

Figure 2.1 Functional components of a simple computer system

In physical terms in the smallest computers all of the functional units may be contained in one box. In this case the input device will generally be a keyboard, the output device is likely to be some form of screen or liquid crystal display, the backing storage is likely to be a built-in disk drive and the computer itself may all be housed on a single printed circuit board. In contrast a large computer installation may have a whole network of many video display units each acting as an input and output device, some perhaps located many miles away from the computer centre and connected to the machine via telephone or data transmission cables. In addition a large computer would be likely to have a number of output devices such as printers, plotters etc. The central processing unit of a large computer may well take up several large cabinets and the backing storage will consist of a number of high capacity disk drives. The central processor and disk units will usually be housed in a large, specially designed room or suite and the system will require the services of a number of specialist operators.

Types of computer system

The range of computer systems currently available may be broken down into three broad classifications commonly referred to as 'mainframe computers', 'minicomputers' and 'microcomputers'. The dividing lines between the three groups are very blurred and difficult to define with any precision at least in terms of function. Some of the larger micros perform the same function as the smallest minis, and some of the larger minis are used for the same tasks as the smaller mainframes, but nevertheless the classifications still continue to be used in practice. The salient features of each type are described below.

Mainframe computers

Machines at the largest end of the scale. They are physically large and require purpose-built air-conditioned accommodation and a carefully regulated power supply. They will require specialist operators to control them and will usually be geographically remote from their users. Since the volume of backing storage is huge, often measured in terms of thousands of millions of characters, they are very good at information storage and retrieval and are often used to suppport large tele-processing networks. Such machines excel at tasks requiring the handling of large amounts of data. They will therefore be used by organisations such as banks, large local authorities, central government departments such as the Driver and Vehicle Licensing Centre, or as the central machine of a large company.

Minicomputers

Minicomputers are perhaps the hardest group to define since at one end of the spectrum the larger minis overlap both in appearance and function with the smaller mainframe machines, and at the other end those computers called small minis are virtually indistinguishable from those at the top end of the micro band.

Minicomputers will usually perform rather more slowly than mainframe machines, and are generally aimed at a small number of concurrent uses rather than large user networks. They can therefore be rather smaller, be built rather more cheaply and can be made to be much more tolerant of changes in their operating environment than their mainframe cousins. A typical mid-range mini therefore might have the central processor and disk units contained in a box perhaps the size of two filing cabinets and might serve six or eight remote users. It will not generally require any special power supplies or air conditioning; it will generally operate from a normal 13 amp socket outlet in a normal office environment.

Minicomputers may well be used by smaller firms for the same purpose as larger organisations would use a mainframe, although their capacity as information handling devices is limited by backing storage typically measured in tens or hundreds of millions of characters rather than the thousands of millions of characters which might be normal in a mainframe installation.

Microcomputers

Microcomputers are, in physical terms at least, the smallest end of the scale and are essentially personal. They can be divided roughly into two groups, those at the cheaper end of the scale which are aimed primarily at the hobby or 'games' market, and the remainder aimed at the business sector. A typical large single user micro complete with disks, screen, printer and keyboard can be accommodated on a standard office desk, whilst a small portable system, colloquially known as a lap-top, will have keyboard, screen, processor and disks all in one box small enough to carry in a briefcase and powered by re-chargeable batteries. Whilst micro-computers are essentially single user systems it is possible to link systems together in a number of ways. Over short distances systems may be linked in 'local area networks' (LANs), thus allowing conversation and exchange of data between different machines, and also allowing a number of com-puters to share central resources such as high capacity central disk drives or high speed centralised printers. Over longer distances systems may be linked using either standard telephone lines or dedicated data transmission cables. The connection of systems in this way will usually necessitate the use of a modem (modulator/demodulator) at each end of the line to convert the output signal from the computer into a suitable form for transmission over a normal telephone line (see also chapter 6). Data transmission speeds over long distances using telephone lines will be considerably slower than the speed which could normally be expected using a LAN.

The range of business microcomputers now available is very wide, ranging from machines costing only a few hundred pounds at one extreme to systems costing tens of thousands of pounds at the other. They are very reliable and much publicity centres around their alleged ease of use. After a late start IBM have now, by pure commercial muscle, established the unofficial industry standards, and most micro manufacturers, apart from one or two that have specialised in particular sectors of the market, offer 'IBM compatibility'. This does not necessarily mean that their hardware is constructed in the same way or to the same standards as those manufactured by IBM, they merely claim that their machines will run software written for the IBM range. A survey conducted by *Infomatics* magazine in September 1987, *Infomatics (1987)*, found 53 different manufacturers offering IBM-compatible machines, but beware – some machines are more IBM-compatible than others!

Methods of processing data

Batch processing

In general, present day commercially used computer systems are only capable of executing one instruction at a time. In early systems information was presented to the computer either on punched cards or on punched paper tape, the whole job being prepared before being presented, as a batch, to the machine. The machine then processed the data, working exclusively on that batch until completion before beginning the next task. This method of processing is known as 'batch processing', and is still in use for commercial applications where large amounts of data are required to be processed with little human intervention, for example a large monthly company payroll or the final printing of a bill of quantities. Such a method of operation is ideally suited to this kind of work and many mainframe computers use this approach extensively for commercial data processing.

When using a batch processing approach incoming jobs are 'queued' in an input queue, and output from completed jobs will be placed onto an output queue. A diagrammatic representation is shown in figure 2.2. Although in early systems the information was presented on cards or punched tape it is now much more likely to be submitted via a video display terminal. Most commercial systems will allow multiple input queues to allow jobs to be processed according to criteria set by the system operations manager. Examples of such criteria might include the time of submission (a simple first come first served approach), but this is likely to be modified by factors such as the priority requested by the user (higher priorities often incur a premium charge for faster turnaround), and the level of processing resources required to do the job (processes expected to generate large amounts of print or jobs requiring special arrangements may be given a lower priority by the system manager because of the resources required).

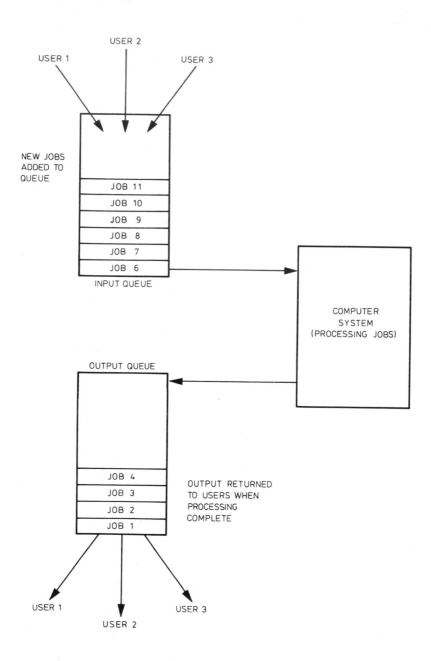

Figure 2.2 Batch processing

Interactive processing

Batch processing is clearly suited to extensive data processing operations where the user is prepared to submit his information for subsequent processing and does not expect an instantaneous reply. It is plainly not suited to operations such as the interrogation of a database, where a speedy response is required. In order to cope with this type of processing an alternative approach, called 'interactive processing', is often employed.

For this type of work the time taken by the operator in keying in the enquiry and the time taken by the computer in passing the result back to the user is very long when compared with the speed at which the computer can actually process a request. It therefore follows that if batch processing techniques were to be used the processor would be idle for a substantial proportion of the total time. In this case therefore the computer no longer concentrates on one job to the exclusion of all others, but instead divides the available processor time cyclically among the users, giving each user exclusive use of the computer for a fixed period of time before saving the task being processed and proceeding to the next user. Each user is therefore allocated a 'slice' of the available processing power, and the process is known as 'time slicing'. A diagrammatic representation is shown in figure 2.3.

The time slicing approach is a great improvement on batch processing techniques, and in a well balanced installation gives each user the illusion of having exclusive use of the machine. The system is however critically reliant upon the correct balance being maintained between the number of users and the central processing power available if response times for individual users are not to become unreasonably long. Once the number of users passes the critical level the performance of the system degrades rapidly, and the only solution is to add more processing power. In addition the amount of disk storage available may well need to be increased as the number of users increases. The approach therefore lacks a certain amount of flexibility and requires very careful management if it is to be successful. Many minicomputer systems are based upon this philosophy.

Distributed processing

In an attempt to overcome the difficulties posed by the above systems, and to meet the increasing demand from users for 'desk-top' computer power, the approach now adopted by many large organisations has been to distribute processing power from the centre to the users in the form of

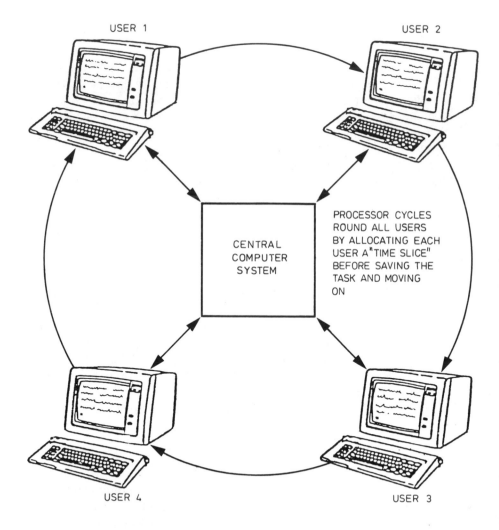

Figure 2.3 Interactive processing

microcomputers used as intelligent terminals to the central machine. Such a system is known as 'distributed processing', and is illustrated diagrammatically in figure 2.4. Terminals may be equipped with their own disk drives and printers, and such systems will normally allow authorised users the right to both process data locally and also transfer information to and from the centre, subject of course to operational controls. Systems such as this will also usually act as a kind of local area network allowing users to communicate with each other via the central machine.

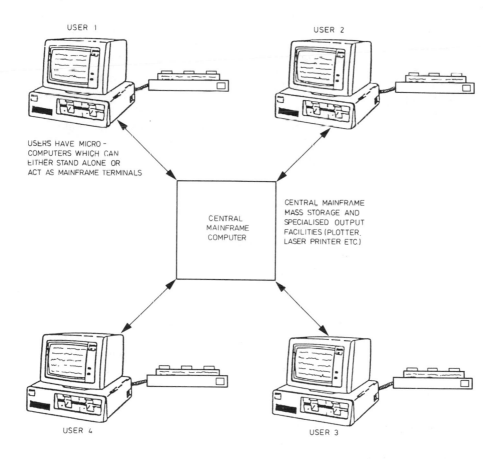

USER 1

USER 2

USERS HAVE MICRO -
COMPUTERS WHICH CAN
EITHER STAND ALONE OR
ACT AS MAINFRAME TERMINALS

CENTRAL
MAINFRAME
COMPUTER

CENTRAL MAINFRAME
MASS STORAGE AND
SPECIALISED OUTPUT
FACILITIES (PLOTTER,
LASER PRINTER ETC.)

USER 4

USER 3

Some commonly quoted measures of size and performance

Microcomputer manufacturers usually describe the 'size' of a system by defining the storage capacity of the central processing unit, sometimes called the main memory, and the total amount of backing storage (usually disk space) accessible by the processor at any one time. The 'size' of the central processor is usually quoted in 'bytes', where 1 byte generally equals 1 character, but because the numbers tend to be large it is conventional to give the information in 'K' bytes (KB) where $K=2^{10}$ or 1024. Sometimes KB is colloquially abbreviated simply to K, so a machine described as having 256K (256KB) of main memory will therefore have a central processing unit with the ability to store 256×1024 characters of information. This measure is important since information held in main memory can be manipulated much more quickly than information held on disk, and it is therefore likely that the larger the main memory the faster the machine will be able to process complex programs using sizeable volumes of data.

The amount of backing storage available is also usually given in bytes, but because the numbers tend to be even larger than for main memory, figures tend to be quoted in 'M' bytes (MB) where $M = 2^{20}$ or 1 048 576. 1MB therefore = $1K^2$ bytes. As an indication of what this means in terms of text, Gooch(1986:p13) estimates that 1MB is approximately equivalent to 400 average A4 pages. Backing storage figures for larger computers, particularly mainframes, may be given in Giga-bytes (GB) where 1GB = 2^{30}.

Whilst such measures are useful in gauging the capacity of a system they say nothing at all about its performance. It is rather like saying a car has four seats. In addition to the above therefore some manufacturers quote the speed at which the processor operates, usually in cycles per second quoted in mega-hertz (MHz), but this again tells a prospective user little about how well the machine will actually perform a particular task in a working environment; to return to the car analogy the measures we have so far are equivalent to the number of seats and the maximum speed of the engine.

What the prospective buyer really wants is some way of comparing how well each of the machines on offer will do the job, and the most often used way of attempting this is to construct some hypothetical test data consisting of a mix of representative operations which can then be processed on each machine, the results being compared one with another. Such tests are usually termed 'benchmarks', and as Jones (1987) says:

> Good benchmarks should compare systems doing the same tasks, and ideally those tasks should closely resemble the ones users will actually want to carry out.

One set of benchmarks developed to test the calculation speed of micro-computers has been developed by the magazine *Personal Computer World* and is described in Walker (1986). Benchmarks can of course also be developed to compare the performance of a number of software packages on the same machine, rather than of the machines themselves, and an example of a set developed to compare the relative performance of micro-computer based data manipulation packages is shown in Lang (1986).

The problems of comparing computer performance are not, of course, new or limited to microcomputers. With larger computers the problems become more complex and the units of measurement more numerous. Among the best known are 'Mips' (millions of instructions per second), 'Mflops' (millions of floating point operations per second) and the Whetstone test, a mix of typical programming instructions. A table of some of the more widely used measures for large computers is given in Jones (1987), although Jones is rather sceptical both about the way in which some manufacturers express the test results and even about the usefulness of the measures themselves:

> But there is a basic problem with all types of benchmarks. Their relevance to any user's problem depends on how closely the processing task used for the benchmark matches the task the user wants to carry out

Nevertheless Jones reports a senior executive employed by a large computer manufacturer as saying:

> What our sales force and customers want is a number however good or bad.

Input devices

Video display terminals

These devices currently provide the most popular and widely used method of interactive communication between the user and the computer, and all modern computers will have at least one. The unit is connected to the computer by a cable, and information typed via the keyboard is transmitted to the processor. Terminals may communicate with the host computer either on a character-by-character basis or the input may be 'buffered' within the terminal until some special key, often the 'carriage return' or 'enter' key is pressed. Responses from the computer are displayed on the screen.

Most keyboards will have the main character keys set in the normal typewriter style (often called the QWERTY pattern after the arrangement of the characters on the top row), although other patterns have been tried from time to time. All terminals will also have other special purpose keys as well, and many terminals have 'function' keys, the meaning of which can be controlled from within particular programs.

Screen displays are available in a range of colours, green characters on a black background perhaps being the most often used although yellow or orange on black and either black on white or white on black are also popular. Some computers can use colour display terminals which allow output to be displayed in a range of colours although the resolution particularly with the cheaper models is often poor. Some special (and usually expensive) terminals have the ability to display high resolution computer generated drawings, and such screens are commonly used for computer aided design applications.

Optical mark recognition (OMR), magnetic ink character recognition (MICR) and optical character recognition (OCR)

These systems, as the names suggest, are all attempts to 'read' information either written or printed on paper.

Optical mark recognition relies on the location by a scanning device of written marks (generally indicating a 'yes' response) or the absence of marks (usually indicating a 'no' response) on a pre-printed form. It is obvious that OMR techniques are therefore very useful for jobs such as the evaluation of data gathered during market research studies. The limitations of OMR techniques are the limited range of input options, and the fact that the forms must be manufactured to reasonable tolerances and must be kept clean if spurious entries are to be avoided, although some systems do overcome the dirt problem with the use of special graphite pencils. Typical data capture speeds are between about 25 000 and 30 000 characters per minute.

The logical progression from OMR is the recognition of actual characters rather than just marks on a piece of paper. The first method evolved entailed printing the characters in a special magnetic ink in a very stylised type font, the characters then being scanned electronically. This method is known as magnetic ink character recognition, and is perhaps most widely known for its use by banks for sorting and processing cheques.

MICR is however only of use where the characters can be printed on the page in magnetic ink. A different approach is required to recognise characters written on an ordinary document, and this has led to the development of optical character recognition (OCR) systems. Most OCR readers examine each character as if it were made up of a pattern of tiny dots. When the whole pattern has been scanned the pattern detected is compared with a set of standard patterns held in the machine and when a reasonable match is found that character is considered to be the one read. If no match can be achieved within the tolerances allowed then a read error occurs and the character is flagged as an error. Two standard character sets were originally used, OCR 'A' and OCR 'B', but OCR readers are now available which can cope with typewritten documents. Much more development is required before OCR techniques can be applied to hand-written documents. Modern OCR readers will operate at about 2400 characters per second but are conventionally operated at much slower speeds for greater accuracy. A potted history of OCR and an indication of future research in this field was given in Howard (1986).

A number of companies have experimented with OCR systems to read in bills of quantity for subsequent processing by contractors estimating packages and an example of such a system is described in Lane (1985). Perhaps the most promising initiative in this area is the development, in America, of a hand-held scanning device reported by Bajarin (1987) and now available in the United Kingdom. Such a device will vastly increase the scope for this type of data input. However whilst the technical prob lems of transferring text from typewritten copy into the computer may soon be solved, the software required to interpret the words is very complex.

Digitisers and graphics tablets

A digitiser (and its smaller brother the graphics tablet) is a form of input device which permits co-ordinate information to be taken from a drawing directly using an electronic pen to either trace around shapes or 'pick off' particular points. Conventional digitisers work by having a very fine matrix of wires embedded in the board which register a signal in both horizontal and vertical directions when the board is touched with the special pen. The computer can therefore calculate the X and Y co-ordinates of the point selected by the pen, and suitable software can then calculate distances between points using conventional co-ordinate geometry. Such devices are of obvious use in computer aided measurement (see also chapter 9).

An unusual form of digitiser is that used by Techsonix in connection with their computer aided measurement software. This system uses ribbon microphones positioned along the X and Y axes of the board and the signal is produced by a special pen which generates an ultra-sonic sound when pressed onto the board.

Digitisers are available to accommodate A3, A2, A1 and A0 size drawings, and smaller graphics tablets are available to accommodate A4 size sheets. The price increases rapidly with the size.

Pressure pad and similar devices

These devices usually consist of either a pressure pad or a solid state board similar to a digitiser. Information is written by hand onto a sheet of paper laid over the board, the characters written are deciphered by a small in-built microprocessor and the resultant code is transmitted to the host computer. Such devices are of obvious benefit although the units available at the time of writing tend to be expensive, are limited in size and can only 'read' capital letters.

Hand held data collection devices

An interesting recent development is the introduction of the 'pocket computer' which can be used out of the office as a hand held data collection device. One such machine was reviewed in Gross-Niklaus (1987), who describes a unit 140mm x 80mm x 30mm containing 32K ROM and 16K RAM with a two-line, 32-character liquid crystal display. Backing storage is provided by exchangeable 32K plug-in RAM packs. The unit also has an optional communications link allowing data gathered in the field to be down-loaded to a larger machine upon return to the office.

Devices such as this offer great potential for use on site, perhaps during the post contract stage, and their use can be expected to spread rapidly. The introduction of a modified version of such a device used as an electronic field book for land survey data is described in *Computer Weekly* (1988).

Output devices

Printers

Printers comprise a very wide range of machines indeed. Beginning at the largest end of the scale, the printers used by a large mainframe computer are physically large (typically a free-standing cabinet say 1200mm x 1000mm x 1500mm high), generally capable of printing a complete line of 132 characters at once. Mechanical printers are still widely used and are capable of speeds up to say 2000 lines per minute, but the newer machines employ a laser printing technology and speeds of over 10 000 characters per second are claimed.

Until very recently, the vast majority of printers sold for mini and microcomputers were mechanical, and were either of the daisy-wheel or dot-matrix type. In recent months, however, small laser printers have become extremely popular and the market share of daisy-wheel printers has rapidly declined. Printers used for micro and minicomputers tend to be much smaller, slower and cheaper than the printers used on mainframe computers.

Daisy-wheel printers take the name from the type of wheel, a plastic or metal wheel with the character set arranged on individual stalks radiating from the centre giving a flower-like appearance. A wide variety of different fonts is available by changing the print wheel, and the main advantage of the daisy-wheel printer is the print quality which is indistinguisable from that produced by an electric typewriter. The main disadvantage is the speed which is limited to about 55 characters per second.

Matrix printers generate the characters from a pattern of dots formed by pressing small needles against the paper via a conventional typewriter style ribbon. Most matrix printers will possess the ability to print either at high speed in 'draft' mode (say up to about 450 characters per second), or to print what is known as 'near letter quality' (NLQ) by building up more fully formed letters from multiple passes across the document. Near letter quality print is therefore much slower than the draft mode, but nevertheless does produce a very acceptable typewriter-style text. Most matrix printers have the facility to print a number of different fonts, at different pitches and with text in different sizes, even changing from one to another actually in the body of a document; they are thus much more flexible than the daisy-wheel type.

As noted earlier, small laser printers developed by companies such a Xerox and Canon using state of the art electrostatic printing techniques are rapidly gaining ground in small computer installations, due mainly to their ability to produce virtually any style of print very quickly, very quietly, with superb clarity at speeds up to about twenty pages per minute. Laser printers are becoming very popular when used in connection with 'desktop publishing' software (see also chapter 5). The main disadvantage of laser printers at present is the relatively high cost but no doubt this will be overcome in time.

Other types of printer, based on alternative technologies, are also available; for example, some manufacturers use an ink-jet mechanism whilst others use a thermal technique using special paper. Such machines are however at the moment very much in the minority. Printer technology is however constantly changing, but Stobie (1988) contains a good review of the contemporary scene. Stobie also comments that significant technological improvements now mean that ink-jet printers may be about to make a significant impact on the market. Such machines have advantages over laser printers in that they can print on continuous stationery, can handle paper of greater width, are as quiet or quieter in operation and can print in a number of different colours.

Plotters

Plotters are used to enable the output of drawn information from the computer, and the principal use therefore tends to be in computer aided design although small plotters are sometimes used for the production of graphs and charts. Plotters may be of two basic configurations:

i) 'Drum' plotters use a continuous roll of paper moved by rollers, and pens fixed to a carrier which allows movement across the paper. The main advantage of this type is that, whilst the width of drawing which can be produced is limited by the width of the rollers, the length is unlimited. It is therefore possible to produce very large drawings. Disadvantages are that the plotting speed tends to be slower than the 'flat bed' type, and it is very difficult to use pre-printed paper.

ii) 'Flat bed' plotters have a table upon which standard size sheets of paper are secured, and units are available in a range of sizes capable of handling paper ranging from A4 to double A0. Prices rise sharply as the size increases. Plotting speeds may be higher than for drum plotters.

Plotters may be connected 'on-line' to the computer for direct plotting, but in a large computer system the plotter output is more likely to be spooled on a magnetic tape or similar medium for plotting 'off-line' (i.e. independently of the main computer).

A variety of different types of plotting mechanisms is used, but the most common has removable pens using either liquid ink, roller-ball or fibre tip in a range of colours. Plotters using electrostatic technology are however gaining ground in some areas of work, principally due to their ability to print 'full colour' drawings.

Backing storage devices

Magnetic tape units

Magnetic tape storage is probably the most widely used form of computer readable secure storage. Some early micro systems used cassette tapes of the kind used in portable tape recorders, but modern cassette systems use special cassettes which are much larger, more expensive, can store much more information and can be accessed much more quickly. Mini and mainframe systems use special computer tape reels ¾" wide with either seven or nine recording tracks. Information is encoded as patterns of magnetic dots across all tracks. The principal disadvantage of magnetic tape systems is that the information must be accessed serially, i.e. to find a specific piece of information it is necessary to begin at the beginning of the tape and read each record in turn until the required information is found. This obviously means lengthy (at least by computer standards) search times if the required information is near the end of the tape.

Magnetic disk units

The most widely used backing storage devices are magnetic disk units. Each disk consists of a flat platter coated on both sides with a magnetic recording medium. Information is encoded on the disk as a pattern of magnetic dots in concentric circles (called 'tracks') usually on both sides of the disk. Disks therefore overcome the main problem encountered when using magnetic tape, that is that information can only be accessed serially beginning from the start of the tape. With disks, in addition to dividing each surface into tracks, surfaces may also be divided into sectors, and the tracks sub-divided into blocks. Direct addressing of information is therefore possible by quoting the appropriate track/sector/block address.

In large systems several disks may be mounted one above another on a common spindle and the resultant assembly is known as a disk 'pack'.

Three main types of magnetic disk are in common use and are shown diagrammatically in figure 2.5.

Fixed head drives
As the name suggests the read/write heads in these units do not move, and it therefore follows that they need a separate read/write head for each track. The speed of access is thus very fast indeed, but they also tend to be the most expensive. Fixed head disks are not generally removable, and will usually only be found on mainframe or the larger minicomputers. Storage capacities are likely to be measured in gigabytes.

Hard disk moving head devices
These devices only have one read/write head for each recording surface rather than a separate head for each track, and the head is therefore required to move across the disk, usually by means of a stepper motor. Where the disk is 'fixed', (i.e. non-removable) as for example the 'Winchester' technology disks commonly found in desk-top micro-computers, the read/write heads will usually be the 'take off and land' type which rest on the disk surface whilst the disk is stationary and 'fly' as the disk begins to spin. Where the disk is removable however the head must be initially held away from the disk and loaded towards it when the disk has reached operational speed. Devices of this type are used on all types of computer, although for mainframe systems they have tended to be displaced by 'head per track' units because of the faster access times required where large volumes of data are concerned. Typical storage capacities might range from 20MB on a desk-top micro to several hundred MB for a mainframe unit.

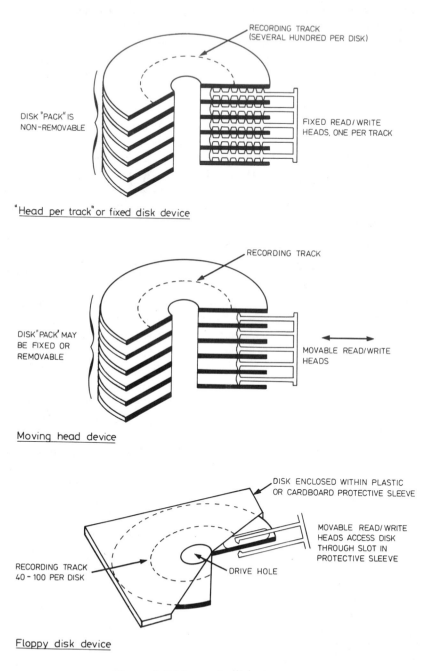

Figure 2.5 Magnetic disk storage

Floppy disk or 'diskette' systems

These units comprise the smallest members of the magnetic disk family. A floppy disk consists of a thin plastic disk coated on both sides with a magnetic recording medium and contained within a cardboard or plastic dust cover. A number of different sizes of disk are in common use including 3", 3.5", 5.25" and 8" diameter. Floppy disk systems are much slower than hard disk devices and, unlike hard disks which revolve all of the time, floppy disks generally only spin when they are actually being accessed. They are extensively used in microcomputer systems, and storage capacities may vary from about 256KB to around 1MB.

Optical disks

Optical disk technology has been around since the late 1970s, and during the period since the mid 1980s a number of systems have been built which integrate video-disk playback systems and contemporary computer technology. Perhaps the best known application is the BBC 'Doomsday' project, described in Linderholm (1987). Data is stored on optical disk by 'burning' small pits in the surface with a laser, and may later be retrieved by scanning again with a laser beam. Such systems have, for a number of years, been proposed as an alternative to magnetic disk. The principal advantages are seen as being the ease with which visual information can be stored and accessed by computer database management software, coupled with an increase in the amount of information which could be stored on a disk of any given size. The major disadvantage however is that once the data is written to the disk it cannot currently be subsequently erased. The computer industry, with its insatiable appetite for acronyms, refers to such systems as WORM (Write Once Read Many times) technology.

A report published in 1987 by a leading research company (Wharton (1987)) predicts a big growth in systems built around optical disks during the 1990s, predicting total sales of such systems at £66m by 1991 compared with only £2.5m in 1986. Optical disk units are now offered for use with personal computers, and a number of manufacturers are believed to be close to offering systems which will allow information to be erased or overwritten.

Linking computers together

To the normal person in the street it is unbelievable that, although the computer industry is considerably less than half a century old, is a child of this wonderfully co-ordinated twentieth century, and represents the absolute pinnacle of mankind's highest technological achievement, it is nonetheless not possible to take a disk containing information prepared on one type of computer (for example an Apricot Xi) and read it directly into another type of computer (for example an IBM PC). Not only do computers use a bewildering range of disk sizes, but even when the disk size is the same, and even if the same software package is implemented on both machines, there are any number of different formats in which the data may be recorded which form a barrier between one machine and another. In order therefore to transfer information between, for example an Apricot and an IBM PC, it is necessary to resort to connecting the computers together with pieces of wire, reading the information from the Apricot disk into the Apricot computer, using some software in the Apricot to transmit the data down the wire, using some more software in the IBM machine to catch it, and finally writing the data to an IBM disk.

In view of the lamentable lack of co-ordination between one manufacturer and another, it is perhaps fortunate that the computer industry has been able to develop interface protocols to allow data to be exchanged electronically, and there are now software packages available for all of the popular machines which will perform the required transmission and reception functions. Unfortunately the electronic transmission of information is still not so easy as it sounds since both the source computer and the target computer need to have the relevant software loaded in order that the data can be successfully transferred; the process is analogous to a telephone call which requires the attention of both parties if a successful transfer of information is to take place.

Local Area Networks (LANs)

Sooner or later an organisation which uses large numbers of stand-alone desk-top computers will begin to consider the possiblity of connecting them together, either to allow data to be transferred from one machine to another, or to allow a number of computers to access common central facilities such as high capacity disks or perhaps high speed laser printers.

Where a number of computers are to be connected together over short distances (say within the same building) the most common method is to construct some kind of local area network or LAN. There are many types of network, but all are essentially based on either a 'star' format where each separate user or 'node' is connected directly to a central network server, a 'ring' format where all of the nodes are connected together to form a continuous endless loop, or a 'bus' format where the two most distant 'nodes' are connected together and all other nodes form branches from this main cable. Each is shown diagrammatically in figure 2.6. In addition to the physical cabling required, networks will also require some software running in all of the separate nodes to control access to and traffic on the

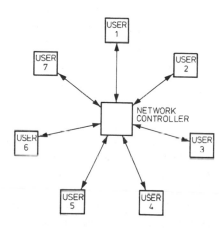

MESSAGES PASSED FROM USER –
USER VIA CENTRAL CONTROLLER

Star network

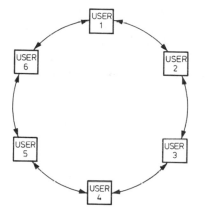

MESSAGES PASSED AROUND THE
RING MAY ONLY BE "CAUGHT" BY
THE USER TO WHOM THEY ARE
ADDRESSED

Ring network

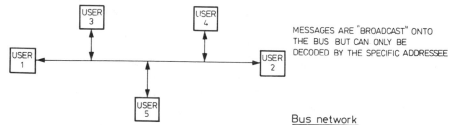

MESSAGES ARE "BROADCAST" ONTO
THE BUS BUT CAN ONLY BE
DECODED BY THE SPECIFIC ADDRESSEE

Bus network

Figure 2.6 Basic network types

network itself. Note that this software does not normally prevent the nodes from working as stand-alone computers in their own right, but does allow them to communicate with each other should the need arise. An excellent introduction to the practicalities of local area networks is given in Malcolm (1987a) and Malcolm (1987b).

Long distance communication

Where communication is required over long distances, the most common method is to use telephone lines. The cheapest method, although it does have disadvantages, is to use the normal public switched telephone network, but greater transmission speeds can be achieved by using a private wire.

The main problem with data transmission via the telephone system is that the signals generated by the computer must be modulated in order to make them suitable for transmission through the telephone system, and subsequently de-modulated by the receiving computer. This process generally involves the use of a supplementary box of electronics known as a 'modem' (Modulator/De-Modulator) attached to each computer. Another major problem in using British telephone equipment has been the very slow data transfer speeds, due principally to the use of electro-mechanical switching equipment in the telephone exchanges, but these problems are steadily being overcome by the introduction of electronic telephone exchanges and fibre optic cables.

There are a variety of different protocols in use for the transfer of data in this way. Toothill (1987) contains a useful overview of the major public-domain communication protocols, together with an introduction to the kinds of problems likely to be encountered in practice. Modems and communication protocols are considered in more detail in chapter 6.

References

Bajarin T. (1987) 'Microsoft signs up with Alps for handheld scanners' *Personal Computer World* Vol.10 no.8 (August 1987) p. 90

Brandon P. S. and Moore R.G. (1983) *Micro Computers in Building Appraisal* Granada

Computer Weekly (1988) 'Survey data captured' *Computer Weekly* 14.1.88 p. 32

Feigenbaum E. and McCorduck P. (1983) *The Fifth Generation* Addison Wesley

Gooch B. (1986) *The Computer Guide for Builders* Privately published

Gross-Nicklaus M. (1987) 'Psion organiser II' *Personal Computer World* Vol.10 no.8 (August 1987) pp. 114–118

Howard A. (1986) 'Character Recognition' *Systems International* November 1986 p. 69–70

Infomatics (1987) 'Survey' *Infomatics* September 1987 pp. 80–92

Jones P. (1987) 'Odious comparisons' *Infomatics* December 1987 pp. 60–64

Lane K. (1985) 'Bills made easy' *Construction Computing* Summer 1985 p. 23

Lang K. (1986) 'Screentest – PC File' *Personal Computer World* Vol.9 no.12 (December 1986) pp. 168–171

Linderholm O. (1987) 'A machine for all times' *Personal Computer World* January 1987 pp. 160–165

Malcolm P. (1987a) 'Run around the clock' *Personal Computer World* February 1987 pp. 122–126

Malcolm P. (1987b) 'Caught in the net' *Personal Computer World* May 1987 pp. 134–138

Stobie I. (1988) 'Silence is golden in the printing marketplace' *Computer Weekly* 14.1.88 pp. 30–31

Toothill P. (1987) 'Clearing the line' *Personal Computer World* April 1987 pp. 174–176

Walker N. (1986) 'Time's (nearly) up!' *Personal Computer World* Vol.9 no.12 (December 1986) pp. 164–167

Wharton (1987) *Image processing* Wharton Information Systems

Widdeson P. (1980) *Computers and Public Authorities* Privately published

3 The Selection and Management of an Office Computer System

Objectives

At the end of this chapter you should be able to:

- Discuss the factors to be considered when choosing an office computer system.
- Discuss the management problems inherent in the introduction and subsequent successful day-to-day operation of an office computer system.
- Develop a management and training strategy to enable new systems to be introduced as painlessly as possible.

Choosing an office computer system

A common problem with the introduction of computers in a professional practice is deciding how to go about it. There are pressures from the press, salesmen, often from staff, and from attitudes of 'keeping up with the Jones'. The first steps are often difficult, usually the most crucial, invariably the ones with the most pitfalls.

CICA (1981:p. 8)

Choosing an office computer system, as the above quotation indicates, is often a difficult business, but in many organisations the process is made more difficult than it need be because the decision to acquire a computer is made for the wrong reasons. There are, of course, many reasons why an organisation might want to introduce computers, but among less valid ones might be:

i) to keep up with the Jones – 'all our competitors have computers so we must have one as well'
ii) 'computers are the tool of the future and you ignore them at your peril'
iii) pressure from enthusiastic staff to 'have a go'

All of the above are based on 'feelings', none is based on any kind of rational assessment of the contribution which the machine might make to the organisation as a whole, and whilst the above statements might, at least in part, even be true, an organisation which installs a computer system using any of the above for justification is doomed to disappointment. There is no magic in computer systems; computers will not take an unprofitable business and make it successful. If computer systems are to be used effectively then the application of them must be carefully researched and the costs and benefits must be realistically assessed.

Both Parret & Stead (1986) and Atkin (1987) consider the problem of choice of an office computer system. Essentially what is required is a three-stage process to discover:

i)   Is there a problem?
ii) If there is a problem is a computer solution appropriate?
iii) If a computer solution is appropriate, how is the most suitable system to be chosen, implemented and operated?

Stage 1 – Is there a problem?

This first stage is really part of the routine monitoring process which every business should undertake as a part of its overall business strategy. The questions to be asked therefore are questions about the performance of the business itself:

i)   What are the objectives of the organisation?
ii) Are they being achieved to the satisfaction of the proprietors?
iii) Will the organisation continue, as far as can be foreseen, to achieve them in the future?

Questions such as these should indicate whether any further investigations are justified. If the honest answer to all of the above is 'Yes' then the indications would be that there is no need to undertake detailed investigation of computer systems which might be costly; if however the answer to any of them is 'No' then there is a need to progress to stage 2.

The above scenario views the possible selection and implementation of a computer system very much as the solution to a particular problem. A further question which may arise, particularly, in a forward-looking organisation, might be:

Although I'm satisfied that the organisation is achieving the required objectives at the moment, could computers help me to achieve them more effectively in the longer term?

This question is very much more difficult to answer as it implies the need for some on-going appraisal, research and development. The extent to which an individual organisation will consider this to be worthwhile will obviously depend upon the importance which the organisation attaches to being at the front of the pack. It must be remembered that research and development is a high risk venture which can be very costly.

Stage 2 – What can I do to resolve the problem?

Is the problem simple or complex?

Stage 1 of the process identifies that a problem exists, the next question to be resolved is to decide precisely what the cause of the problem is and what is required in order to overcome it. Some problems may be simple in that one particular process or activity can be seen to be inefficient, but others may have a number of causes; a number of contributory factors may combine together to create the obstruction. Problems such as these may require one composite solution or they may simply be symptomatic of other hidden problems. In any event it is vital to be sure that the precise cause(s) of the problem have been identified before going further.

Having established the precise cause of the problem(s), it is then necessary to ask two further questions:

(1) Would a computer help?
(2) Would use of a computer be cost effective?

The only way to proceed beyond this point is to:

(1) Appoint someone to find out
(2) Establish his or her brief
(3) Review the findings

The analyst

It is at this point that specialist advice is often sought, although in many cases there is no fundamental reason why this should necessitate external consultants. In fact there may be distinct advantages to using someone from within the organisation, provided firstly that some suitable and willing person can be found, and secondly that management recognises that evaluation of this kind may be very time consuming. It is not the kind of work which can be tackled on a 'part-time' basis in addition to existing duties. If however:

(i) the problem is very complex in that it affects a range of activities across the organisation or
(ii) a range of different problems is evident which may necessitate a co-ordinated solution

then an external consultant may prove to be the better choice although the cost is likely to be high.

Hunt (1982b) identifies the qualities which an 'in-house' analyst should possess as:

A suitable candidate for the task must start with an open mind, must have an analytical approach and sufficient knowledge of quantity survey-ing procedures to enable extraction of all relevant information'.

Parrett & Stead (1986), whilst in general agreement with the above, go further:

The person you choose must display the following qualities:

1 Ability to use initiative
2 Self-motivation
3 Willingness to learn and be open-minded – you cannot afford to select someone with tunnel vision
4 Genuine interest in modern technology
5 Analytical ability and preferably a detailed knowledge of the organ-isation and its systems
6 A basic concept of computer programming and a broad knowledge of what computers can do
7 Commitment to the project

It may also be an advantage if the candidate is a user rather than a computer specialist, because a computer specialist might tend to:

(i)   Compromise on management needs in favour of programming needs
(ii) Design systems for ease of programming rather than ease of use
(iii) Fail to analyse the management requirements as well as a user, basically because a user normally knows the existing formal systems and the informal systems which surround them
(iv) Have an in-built bias towards hardware and software with which they are already familiar
(v)   Have a lesser sense of urgency and commitment to the project
(vi) Be unable to look beyond the present application

Above all, the analyst must have the authority to do the job and in particular the authority to investigate and comment on the existing manual procedures. This will inevitably necessitate complete backing from higher management, at either director or partner level as appropriate. The analyst must also of course be given the necessary administrative back-up in the form of secretarial staff, travel facilities and so on.

The analyst's brief

The analyst should be given a brief detailing exactly what is required together with a time scale. The detail of the brief will, of course, vary from organisation to organisation, but remember that this stage is very much a feasibility study; at this stage we are only concerned with ascertaining whether or not a computer system would be feasible, appropriate and cost effective. Remember that the benefits might result either from direct savings in resources, or be due to a reduction in time, or be the result of producing a better product, and the analyst must consider all of these issues. The likely costs and benefits must then be weighed against all of the other ways of solving the problem. All costs must include not only the initial cost of the machine but also the cost of maintenance, staffing, staff training, accommodation for the computer including possible modifications to services such as electric wiring, and the likely cost of lost production whilst the system is installed and commissioned and staff become familiar with its use. A useful and more detailed discussion of some of the financial issues involved is contained in DOC (1980) chapter 8.

At the conclusion of the exercise the analyst should present a full written report for consideration by the board or partners as appropriate and, on the basis of that report, management must then decide whether or not to proceed to stage 3.

Stage 3 – Acquisition and implementation

Having decided, on the basis of the report produced during stage 2, to proceed further, management is now in a position to set an overall budget for the acquisition of the necessary hardware and software, within which it must consider the following points:

(i)   How is the applications software to be chosen?
(ii)   How is the hardware to be chosen?
(iii) Is the equipment to be bought, leased or hired?
(iv)   What maintenance cover is required?
(v)   What operational procedures are required to ensure the integrity of the system?
(vi)   Who will operate the system?
(vii) What training will be required?
(vii) What accommodation will be required?
(viii) Should future expansion be considered?
(ix)   What about the human issues?

How is the applications software to be chosen?

The choice of applications software is by far the most important decision to be made in the acquisition of a computer system. As CICA (1981) points out:

Applications software is the link between the problems you want to solve and their solution by the computer

and Parrett & Stead (1986) stress:

To achieve effective results the user must be able to communicate effectively with the computer in a language which they both understand. It is the software, the computer program, that provides this communicating link...

In general a good software package should be:

(i)   Robust – the package should be fault-tolerant and it should not be possible to break it by hitting invalid keys, for example letters when the system expects numbers or vice-versa, entering an invalid date etc. A good test is to enter 30 February when the system asks for the date. If the software does not pick it up as an error then the chances are the rest of the system is not very robust either.

(ii) Reliable – the package should give the same results consistently and the answers should always be correct. Do not forget that when you buy a program you usually sign a software licence agreement which excludes the vendor from any liability arising from the use of the program. You therefore take full responsibility for the accuracy or adequacy of any results. This might be important for example in the case of programs for the design or selection of structural components. (See also Hunt (1982a).)

(iii) User-friendly – the system should help you to use it. Menus and error messages should be clear and unambiguous. Do not rely on the salesman's demonstration or even your own opinion, get an opinion either from the person who'll have to use it or from someone who's already using it, but treat existing users with some care, people are reluctant to admit they have made a mistake! Very few systems are truly 'user-friendly':

In the words of Trevor Nicholas, Head of Information Systems and Resources, Barclays Bank:

Most (computer) systems are as user-friendly as a cornered rat

(iv) Understandable – the documentation should not only enable you to see how to use the program, but where the program is to do with

design or opinion the documentation should also explain any underlying principles or formulae.

(v) Well supported – for a program of any size there should always be
some form of support service. Ask the vendor what you'd have to do
to get assistance if the program failed in the middle of a vital run at
4pm on Christmas Eve! Ask about future updates to the system.

Carter (1984) reports that the Chartered Institute of Building Services
Computer Applications Panel is to publish algorithms for solution of
building services problems, and argues that the professional institutions as
a whole should take some responsibility for establishing testing and valida-
tion procedures for programs which come within their specialist areas.

Acquiring the software

There are essentially only three ways in which software can be obtained:

(i)   'Off the shelf'
(ii)   In-house development
(iii) Specially commissioned from a software house

'Off the shelf' software

There is a very wide range of 'off the shelf' software available for many of
the more standard applications, for example word processing, spreadsheet
calculators, data manipulation, accounting, project scheduling etc. If these
are the applications required then it is highly likely that a suitable program
can be found off the shelf.

Hunt (1982a) gives a general checklist of points to examine, and Barrett
(1987b) offers a series of criteria for the evaluation of project management
software. Both lists include the general characteristics described above in one
form or another, and the following general rules may be derived:

(i)   How heavy duty is it? Will it contain all the information you need to
process, not only now but in the forseeable future?
(ii)   Can it do all of the things you want to do?
able?
(iv)   How easy is it to use? How difficult is it to break? Are the error
messages easy to understand?
(v)   Does it process the data fast enough?
(vi)   How well supported is the package? How good is the documentation, is there a user 'hotline', how much training is included/

available? Is there an established user base to whom you can talk before you buy?

(vii) How much does maintenance cost? How much is the next upgrade?

(viii) What machines will it run on? What operating system does it need?

(ix) Will the operators need to be re-trained when the supplier issues the next release

The correct choice of software supplier is also vitally important if the installation is to be trouble free. The documentation supplied with many systems is often difficult for the naive user to understand, and the supplier is often the lifeline in the event of a problem. He must therefore not only have a complete understanding of the package himself, but must also be able to respond quickly and effectively to purchasers' queries and problems. This may mean either the provision of an adequately manned telephone 'hotline', or a physical presence sufficiently close to the users' office to allow a consultant to be able to sort out users' problems in person.

Finally do not forget that a considerable amount of general purpose software including word processors, spreadsheets etc. is available either free of charge or at very low prices through several bulletin boards (see chapter 5). Whilst such systems can be very good they do, in the main, tend to be unsupported and their use can therefore be something of a gamble.

In-house development

For this option to be even considered the organisation must either have staff already trained who can carry out the work, staff willing to be trained who can be spared from other duties or be prepared to employ trained specialist staff to do the work. Software development in-house is a very expensive activity, and it is most unwise to think that staff who may have written small programs for themselves in the past are capable of writing operational systems for use in an office. The only way that this option can work effectively is for the work to be done by trained computer specialists; it is therefore an option which should be approached with great caution.

On the other hand however this approach is likely to produce the 'best fit' solution for any particular organisation. Most of the currently available quantity surveying packages originated in just this way, and the authors are now attempting to recoup some of the considerable initial outlay by selling the product to other practitioners. The quality of such software is very variable. The development of 'in-house' systems is considered in more detail in chapter 7.

Software specially commissioned from a software house

As might be expected this is by far the most expensive option and the cost of the software is likely to exceed the cost of the hardware. It is however likely to produce a very good 'fit' between the users' requirements and the final computer solution. An organisation following this route could expect to shed all of the responsibilty for production of the software, testing and implementation. The disruptive effects of the installation of the system will therefore be minimised but the cost is likely to be very high.

The actual process of 'purpose-built' software development is considered in more depth in chapter 7.

How is the hardware to be chosen?

In order to select the hardware the organisation's computing philosophy will need to be determined, particularly in terms of the way in which the systems are to be used and the anticipated future degree of expansion. For a small firm purchasing a single machine the problem is fairly simple, but in the case of a larger organisation a decision must be made as to whether to use:

(i)   a number of stand-alone computers, each used for a separate discrete task
(ii)   a number of microcomputers linked in a network
(iii) a large central computer with a number of terminals
(iv)   a distributed processing system with a large central disk

The initial decision will depend largely upon the uses to which the machine is to be put. For example in the case of a system to be used for processing bills of quantity where data for jobs needs to be captured from a number of locations, then a suitable arrangement might be either a large central computer with terminals or a distributed processing system, whereas if the system is simply to be used for *ad hoc* word processing and spreadsheet applications then a better arrangement might be a number of separate computers operating either independently or able to communicate via a local area network. The actual configuration will of course depend on the particular firm concerned, but a critical factor is the number of people expected to use each terminal. There is an obvious conflict here in that, whilst providing a separate terminal on every user's desk might appear to represent the best solution from the human point of view, it is likely to be very expensive and none of the terminals is likely to be used to full capacity. On the other hand if one were to provide a central terminal resource for a number of people then there are bound to be times of conflict, for example when several people need to use the terminal at the same time. Management must therefore decide, as a part of its computing philosophy, which approach the organisation will adopt, and perhaps which users have priority in the event of conflict.

In terms of the particular make or type of computer, the choice may already have been narrowed by the choice of software and the operating system under which it will run. In the case of small computers it is worth remembering that more 'off the shelf' software is available for the IBM range of microcomputers than for any other, but also that some of the machines which describe themselves as 'IBM compatible' represent far better value for money than the IBM machines themselves.

Is the equipment to be bought, leased or hired?

The decision about how to pay for the chosen computer can, as Lawrence (1986) points out, be rather tricky. Whilst the position of any one particular company is likely to be to some extent unique, and changes in tax allowances and interest rates can alter the position, Lawrence offers the following general guidelines:

(i) Only rent or lease for less than two years if you're sure you have no long-term use for the system and aren't worried about the money
(ii) Buy if you've got the money in the bank
(iii) Lease if you aren't worried about the tax concessions and you haven't the money to buy
(iv) Don't lease for as long as seven years, over that period it is cheaper to buy
(vi) Use an operating lease if you want to keep the expenditure off the balance sheet

The best advice is to seek the help of an accountant to assess the precise position at the time.

What maintenance cover is required?

Although modern computers are extremely reliable they do break down from time to time, and adequate cover for maintenance, and repair of the hardware in the event of an equipment failure is obviously of prime importance if the system is to consistently fulfil its purpose.

There are a number of alternative strategies available. It is, of course, possible to 'go bare', in other words to make no specific provision for repair and to simply rely on getting the machine repaired if and when it fails. This is likely, in the long term, to be the cheapest option, but tends to be a risky business since there is no guaranteed response time and it is therefore impossible to predict how long the machine will be out of action. Whilst this might not particularly matter in an organisation using computers in a non-critical way and where an easy return to alternative manual methods is possible, for example simple word processing, it is likely to be of considerable importance where the computer has become established at the centre of a business and perhaps particularly where the computer is used to keep financial records. One may also consider 'going bare' in the case of an organisation using a number of computers of the same type, particularly if there is some inbuilt redundancy, where one computer can be be taken out of service for repair and the work load can be redistributed temporarily onto other machines.

For those organisations adopting a rather more structured policy there are a number of maintenance plans available depending upon the type of equipment installed and the level of service required. At the largest end of the scale, mainframe and minicomputer suppliers will advise on the selection of a suitable maintenance plan, whilst a number of specialist companies exist to serve the microcomputer market.

The cost of a maintenance plan will depend basically upon the level of service required, and companies will prefer to quote for particular installations depending upon the customer's precise requirements, but the cost will largely depend upon the required speed of response. A figure of up to 15 per cent of the initial capital equipment cost per year for example might give a microcomputer installation a guaranteed repair or replacement of faulty equipment within 24 hours.

What operational procedures are required to ensure the integrity of the system?

In addition to documentation detailing the use of each application, operational procedures will also be required in all computer installations to ensure both the continued security of the machine and the data, and also to control/regulate the way in which shared computer resources are to be allocated and the priorities to be given to each task. The formality of such operational procedures will, to a large extent, depend upon the size and complexity of the organisation; in a small firm with perhaps one or two computers the procedures may be very simple, but in a large organisation they will, of necessity, be more complex, but all operational procedures should be written down in an operations manual. Note that whilst security of the majority of a firm's data is a purely domestic concern, where personal data is concerned the Data Protection Act imposes a legal responsibility on data users to ensure that such data is neither lost, accidentally destroyed or subject to unauthorised access (see also chapter 4).

Perhaps the most important aspects of operations procedure, which must be adequately covered regardless of the size of the installation, are those to do with ensuring the security and integrity of both the machine and its data. They will also detail the actions to be taken, and the staff responsible for taking them, in the event of a disaster such as failure of the machine, loss of data, or perhaps even partial or total destruction of the computer facilities for example by fire, flood etc.

Day-to-day physical security of the data

The information stored in a computer system, which might well have been collected over a number of years, may well be much more valuable to an organisation then the equipment itself. The security and integrity of the data is therefore of paramount importance and all systems should contain some procedures to limit the possible consequences of destruction. Excluding vandalism and fraud, which are discussed later, information stored in the computer is under threat from a number of sources including:

- physical damage caused by faulty machinery, for example a defective disk drive may physically damage the disk
- corruption of the information stored on the disk due to a faulty program
- damage caused by lightning strike, power cut or electrical surge rendering the data unreadable
- operator error causing incorrect data to be written to the file
- physical damage resulting from some outside cause. In the case of a hard disk this may be fire, flood etc., but in the case of information stored on floppy disks may be the result of exposure to extreme heat e.g. sunlight through a window, use of the disk as a coffee mat etc., or even loss of the disk itself

The most common method of ensuring day-to-day security of the data is to take security 'back-up' copies on a regular basis. The frequency and extent of the copies will depend upon the type of data and the frequency with which it is usually updated, but most users of hard-disk systems for example will take a complete 'dump' copy of the whole disk perhaps weekly onto either floppy disk or magnetic cartridge tape, with regularly used files perhaps being copied to floppy disk every day. Such a system is known as a 'father/son' arrangement, and it ensures that information can be recovered from a known point in time should any of the above catastrophes occur. Note that with the father/son, or 'single generation' copy arrangement, the copy tape is overwritten each time the information is secured; both the original and the copy are therefore in the machine at the same time, and if a problem occurs during the security operation then both the master and the copy may be lost. The problem may be overcome by using a separate security tape each time, but after a time the number of tapes to be stored becomes unmanageable, and the method tends to be very expensive. A common compromise is to employ either a two or three generation technique where either two or three security tapes are used in rotation. There are therefore always at least two previous copies of the information available at any one time from which the system can be restored.

Remember also to store back-up copies in a safe place away from the computer room; it's not much good having back-up copies of the data from which to restore the system in the event of fire in the computer room if the back-up tapes are themselves destroyed in the fire!

Disaster recovery planning

Disaster recovery planning may be defined as the procedures necessary to allow the organisation to survive partial or total destruction of its computing facilities. It is an aspect of computing which has often been ignored in the past, but the problem is that many companies have become slowly dependent on their computing facilities without realising the implications or the risk to the business if such facilities were either no longer available or were seriously disrupted for a significant period of time. Brown (1987a) claims that, in the financial services sector, computer failure may begin to affect the business within hours although one to four days is typical, whilst Donnelly (1986) reports that a survey carried out by Chubb Insurance Group in America 'records that at least 90 per cent of companies affected by computer disasters went into liquidation within 18 months'.

The extent to which organisations will need to plan for this type of event will, of course, depend upon the size of the installation, and how important that organisation considers its computing facility to be. In the case of a small firm using the kind of microcomputers available in the high street stores it will probably be possible to simply replace damaged equipment with new at very short notice, and provided that the hardware was adequately insured and the data has been adequately preserved the system should be operational again very quickly.

The problem becomes more acute as the installation becomes more complex, and becomes a particular problem when the computer system becomes centralised in one place, for example with a mini or mainframe based installation in particular where specialised power supplies or air conditioning systems are required. In this case a formal disaster recovery plan is essential, and according to Brown (1987a) should include descriptions of:

...facilities necessary to support the minimum processing requirements after a disaster and a tested set of procedures for either the recovery of computer systems or manual fallback.

There are a number of options available. At the lowest level one might make some sort of reciprocal agreement with another company using the same type of equipment, and this might at first sight appear a very cost effective option. The major problem is likely to be that when disaster strikes and you need to make use of the arrangement it may be very difficult for the other company to make sufficient time available to meet your needs.

Another option, which may reduce the total recovery time where the complete computer room is destroyed, is the provision of an alternative computer room ready equipped with the requisite power supplies and air conditioning. This is known as a 'cold start' option and may well reduce the recovery time to weeks rather than months. Other options are 'warm start' where the stand-by computer room is ready equipped with a selected 'cut-down' version of the computer equipment which can provide a reduced service within a few hours, or a 'hot start' facility where an outside firm undertakes to make available a complete installation either immediately or at very short notice. The use of such a system by P&O Containers Ltd which provides a complete replica of its installation at eight hours notice for a cost of £150,000 per annum (1987 prices) is described in Fraser (1987), and Donnelly (1986) describes the use of a number of similar systems costing between £5,000 and £200,000 (1986 prices) per year.

Brown (1987a–f) is a useful series of articles giving more in-depth coverage of the peripheral issues concerned with disaster recovery planning.

Vandalism and fraud

Much has been made in the recent past of the need for computer systems to be 'user-friendly'; to help users to get the best from the system. Unfortunately this factor may also make the systems very vulnerable to access by unauthorised people and may therefore make them susceptible to unauthorised alteration of the information which they contain, either fraudulently or mischievously or both. Whilst the installation is small there may not be a problem, but the problem assumes greater importance the more complex the installation and the more widespread the operation becomes. Norman (1983) classifies a large number of cases revealing the possible effects of computer insecurity, and also discusses the ways in which computer managers can minimise the risk involved. It appears however that many users are unaware of the problem; according to David

Lindsay, Chairman of the British Computer Society security group, reported in Ernest-Jones (1987):

> Most people aren't aware of what security is and that it's needed unless it hits them individually.

It is very difficult to attempt to quantify the extent of computer related crime, because the most successful are either never caught or the victims refuse to make the matter public. Some indication of the size of the problem can be gathered from reports such as McTaggart (1986) which reports an estimated loss to United Kingdom companies of at least £40m per year, and Arthur (1987) which quotes a Confederation of British Industry estimate of between £20m and £30m per year. Whilst the majority of this loss can probably be accounted for through organisations such as the major clearing banks and large public companies, a considerable degree of computer fraud is undoubtedly committed at much lower levels, and is a factor which must be considered by any organisation using computers to handle financial transactions. It has been claimed (*Computer Weekly* (1980)) that at least 80 per cent of detected computer fraud is the result of opportunism

> Computer crime isn't the striped jersey and mask type. It's rather like leaving £5 notes around on the floor and not expecting people to touch them.
>
> (Brian Hitchin, computer security consultant)

Unauthorised access to computer systems may exist at any level for any number of reasons. At the mainframe end of the scale, computers are vulnerable to the kind of attack reported in Holdsworth (1987b), where a group of 'hackers' based in West Germany successfully breached the security of a worldwide computer network run by NASA, and claimed to have examined data stored in 135 different sites, including two in the United Kingdom, over a six-month period. Closer to home is the case of the unauthorised access to the Duke of Edinburgh's Prestel mailbox reported in Holdsworth (1987b). This case also shows the legal problems involved, since although journalists Schifreen and Gold admitted breaking into the system and were initially found guilty of electronic forgery under the 1981 Forgery and Counterfeiting Act, the decision was overruled on appeal by the Lord Chief Justice Lord Lane and the pair were finally acquitted by the House of Lords. On a more domestic level McTaggart (1986) reports the case of a Manchester based building materials supplier which, in the early 1980s operated at a comfortable profit, but by 1984 following the introduction of a computer based stock control and invoicing system was operating at a considerable loss. In this case the problem was found to be unauthorised alteration by counter staff of the prices in the system. Goods were then supplied to accomplices in the trade at below cost price.

On the larger machines the security and integrity issues are, of course, taken very seriously by the manufacturers and suppliers, and it is perhaps microcomputers, and particularly microcomputers connected in networks, which are most susceptible to the opportunist. Kochanski (1986) sums up the problem:

> Microcomputers are a familiar sight in an increasing number of offices; but it's still remarkable how little thought is given by the average user to the sensitivity of information held on the system. People who would not dream of leaving filing cabinets unlocked have no objection to leaving computers accessible, with exactly the same information in them.

Kochanski also summarises the main threats to data security and integrity:

> First, detectable alteration, where someone erases a report that took days to prepare; second, undetectable alteration, such as adding false invoices to the purchase ledger; third, detectable reading, where a disk containing the customer mailing list goes missing; and fourth, undetectable reading, where a maintenance engineer makes a copy of the file containing next year's business plan and takes it with him.

The solution to some of these problems relies on physical security. Floppy disks, and back-up copies, containing sensitive data should be locked away, and it is possible to fit the microcomputers and terminals themselves with a Yale type lock to prevent unauthorised usage.

At the software level the most common protection is the 'password', some secret combination of characters which must be entered before the computer will allow access to particular systems or data files. There are however a number of factors which should be considered if passwords are to remain effective:

(i) Passwords must, of course, be meaningful to the user if they are to be easily remembered, but they must be sufficiently obscure that they cannot easily be guessed. Passwords such as 'FRED', the user's name or 'chairman' represent no protection at all.

(ii) Passwords must be changed often; the longer a password stays unchanged the greater the number of people likely to learn it.

(iii) Passwords must be kept confidential to those who need to know them and this will normally mean that they must not be written down; stories of passwords being written on the side of terminals are commonplace, and one computer security adviser is reported in Ernest-Jones (1987) as knowing of a bank which has a notice in its payment room saying 'Today's password is....'

(iv) It is little use having users password-protect their files if the operating system passwords are left as set by the supplier. Access at the operating system level will often allow hackers to read a complete list of user passwords, and it has been estimated (Holdsworth (1987b)) that probably 30 per cent of users leave the manufacturer's password on their system.

Although passwords are by far the most commonly used security device there is widespread belief among computer professionals that they are inadequate for all but the lowest level of security. Other methods which are now beginning to be used include:

(i)   file encryption systems, where the contents of a file are 'coded' and can only be unlocked with the correct 'key'. One such system is described in Kochanski (1986).
(ii) 'keyboard dynamics' where the computer operating system establishes and monitors a user's identity by understanding the unique way in which that user taps the keys.
(iii) the use of 'mandatory' operating systems, described in Holdworth (1987a), where the operating system monitors users and decides whether or not to give access on the basis of a profile of each user containing details of the type of information he is allowed to access, the time of day during which he usually works etc.
(iv) the development of automatic 'auditing' routines which record everything which happened inside the computer.

Finally a reminder that computer security does not end even when you sell the machine. Barrett (1987a) reports the case of a student who purchased a second hand computer from an army-surplus store, and later found that he had got 'about 1,500 sensitive files' from the Royal Signals and Radar Establishment, Malvern, including lists of staff, departmental costings, lists of equipment and correspondence with suppliers.

Who will operate the system?

Arrangements to actually use the system will, of course depend upon the software to be installed. In the case of a single-user system which will only be used by one person, for example a word processing system, the answer is simple, but the question requires more thought in the case of a multi-user system or a single-user system which is to be used by a number of different people. In this case it is essential to have some one person in control and responsible for the day-to-day running of the computer, including backing up data in accordance with the procedures laid down in the operations manual, ensuring that printers are supplied with paper and ribbons, maintaining stocks of consumables such a floppy disks, liaison with maintenance contractors etc. A most important function of the computer operator in this situation is that of supporting other users, particularly those who are new or those who only have a need to use the computer occasionally and may therefore need help and guidance.

In the case of a small installation using 'off-the-shelf' software, experience seems to show that the operator need not necessarily have specialist computer training, and the size and complexity of the organisation will determine whether or not the supervision of the computer is a separate full-time job. It should however be remembered that some arrangement needs to be made to cover holiday periods, sickness etc. and there should therefore be at least one more employee who can take over at short notice should the need arise.

What training will be required?

Training is one of the most difficult areas to plan satisfactorily, and yet adequate staff training is essential if an organisation is to get the best from its computer investment. Experience also appears to show that this is probably the one area above all others in which management try to economise. Powell (1987), reporting on research carried out in 1985, states that on average, for a new system, management allocated only one day to training and this tended to be largely on a seminar consisting of a demonstration of the system. Even when more comprehensive training programmes are available the result is not always totally satisfactory. Andrew (1987) examines the question of training in a number of quantity surveying practices which had recently introduced a computerised billing system, and found that although the firms were not disappointed with the quality of the training offered, in fact the three-day programmes themselves were rated by many as very good, nonetheless:

> The survey revealed that not all firms feel that they have achieved extensive utilisation of the system, and that many who have achieved this level have only done so after a lengthier period than originally anticipated.

There is an instinctive feeling that the best way to learn to use computers is by trial and error, and there is no doubt that it is possible to learn this way, provided that management does not expect the system to be in operational use at the same time. The basic mistake which is made over and over again is to expect that a computer system will be working at full capacity almost within hours of installation. This hardly ever happens, and whilst management might well be unwilling to spend money on formal training courses it must nonetheless be prepared to allow staff the opportunity to gain familiarity with new systems without the pressures imposed in a production environment. Adequate allowance must then be included in the costings for a new computer system to allow for the inevitable loss of productivity which will occur during the familiarisation process.

Although trial and error can result in very good appreciation of the workings of a computer system, it is essentially a random process which relies to a great extent on the availability of a comprehensive manual from which to learn; something which many computer systems lack. In addition the time taken to achieve familiarity with a system on a trial-and-error basis will vary widely from one person to another due to the amount of time likely to be spent in following 'blind alleys'. The contribution which can be made by a formal training course in terms of controlled training over a known period of time should not be overlooked.

Computer-aided training courses, in which the computer itself leads the user through a series of tutorials, are becoming more popular as an alternative to organised group training sessions. Whilst they do have advantages in terms of allowing users to learn at their own pace, they also have significant disadvantages in that their ability to answer queries raised by the user during the session are very limited. The absence of the stimulation which results from the inter-personal contact of a well run group training session is also very difficult to overcome.

Hunt (1987) has much good advice about the training of quantity surveyors in the use of computer techniques.

What accommodation will be required?

Regarding accommodation, the question of where to put the new toy is always a thorny one, and the best solution for any particular organisation will depend upon the particular computing philosophy adopted and the type of computer system installed.

Individual microcomputers working either as stand-alone machines or connected in a network are perhaps the most flexible. Modern micro computers are very tolerant of widely varying environmental conditions, and may therefore be placed almost anywhere within a normal office within reach of an electrical socket, although one should be wary of enclosed alcoves with poor ventilation where over-heating could occur. This flexibility is of course a great help in the development of the kind of user friendly systems now in demand; the executive can have his computer on his desk, and units can be easily positioned at key points around the office for those less fortunate who have to share, but there are other factors to consider, for example:

(i) Microcomputers should be carefully placed to avoid the risk of damage to the machine from knocks, spilled drinks etc.

(ii)   Screens need careful positioning to avoid annoying reflections from lights or windows.

(iii) Modern microcomputers are very portable and therefore easily stolen; one therefore needs to make sure they are adequately protected outside office hours.

(iv)   Remember that the users will need space around the machine to spread out documents etc.

(v)   The need for security of the systems, confidentiality of information etc. might lead to the need to place computers in a separate room and to restrict access.

(vi)   Some types of printer, keyboard and even some computers, are very noisy and may distract others working in the same room.

(vii) Experience seems to show that central computing facilities, a mini-computer or a network server for example, are best placed in a separate room to which access can be restricted if required.

(viii) Although modern computers are very tolerant, do not overlook the possibility that a 'clean' power supply may be required, especially if there is any equipment connected to the circuit which may cause 'spikes' to occur, for example some types of electric motor.

Should future expansion be considered?

Yes, but it is difficult to look further ahead than you can see. The planned operational life of a modern microcomputer system should be taken as no more than about five years; this is not to say that the equipment will be worn out after this length of time, but the technology is advancing at such a rate that systems installed today will be obsolete within this period of time. It is therefore pointless to attempt to plan too far ahead.

It is however very tempting, following the successful implementation of one system, to attempt to add more and more to the original system. This temptation should be viewed very carefully; new applications should be subject to just as searching a scrutiny as was the original in order to assess the cost effectiveness of the proposal. In addition the impact of the new applications on the existing systems must also be carefully considered if degradation of the existing service is to be avoided.

What about the human factors?

Much has been written over the years regarding the human aspects of computing, both from the point of view of human/machine interaction and also with regard to the health and safety of the operators.

Considerable research is presently being carried out to investigate the most effective methods of human/computer interaction, and it has been claimed, see for example Clark (1987a), that many systems operate at only 20 per cent of their potential efficiency because of poor human factor design. The research is however still in its infancy, and it is likely to be a number of years before the results of the latest research initiatives are applied to office systems.

Winfield (1986) offers an excellent introduction to the concepts involved in the human/computer interface problem, including discussions on human psychology and systems design, management of computer projects, computer aided learning and the effects of computerisation on social change.

Much more emotive is the subject of the health and safety of the operator, and concern has been expressed over a number of years about a whole range of illnesses allegedly suffered by the operators of visual-display units (VDUs). Issues of concern have included, amongst others, epileptic fits, radiation, eye problems, effects upon pregnant women, headaches, facial dermatitis, hypertension, repetitive strain injuries and general fatigue. Whilst there have been many studies conducted over the years, none appears to have proved conclusively that the use of VDUs poses any specific medical hazard, although some scientists claim that there is evidence which seems to show that some weak electromagnetic fields similar to those which leak from computers and television sets can trigger allergic symptoms in some subjects including headaches, nausea, sweating, pallor and indigestion. More specifically a survey of over 4 000 staff carried out by the North East London Polytechnic for Newham Borough Council and the local authority trade union NALGO in 1987 (reported in Clark (1987b)) clearly shows that VDU users take more sick leave than non-users, the commonest symptoms being given as muscular aches and pains, eye problems, headaches, tiredness, dizziness and fainting. It is therefore apparent that management must tackle this problem if the introduction of computers is to be successful.

Huws (1987) contains much of interest in this area, and she makes the point that many of the medical problems allegedly caused by computers can be prevented by careful arrangement of the workplace itself. At the ergonomic level, it is vitally important that the user should be comfortable. Many eye problems can be avoided if screens are easy to read with good adjustable contrast and brightness control, adjustable tilt, and are carefully positioned to avoid annoying reflections and glare. Eye problems can also be reduced by limiting the periods of time which a user actually spends looking at a screen. Various limits have been proposed, but a maximum of about one hour at a time followed by at least a fifteen-minute break seems to be an acceptable average, although the report on the Newham survey also recommended that users should spend no more than 50 per cent of their total working time actually working at a VDU. Muscular aches and pains can similarly be eased by the provision of suitable adjustable chairs.

On a psychological level there seems to be some evidence in the Newham survey to support the view that poor job satisfaction often manifests itself in apparent physical symptoms of tiredness, hypertension and irritability. There is also evidence that workers feel that in some cases the computer dictates the pace of the work, that the machine is pushing them along, that they have in some sense lost control, and that this may also give rise to a high incidence of hypertension and similar stress-related illness.

Psychological problems such as these are very complex and in part may impinge on the human/computer interaction issues discussed earlier. Management must however involve staff at all stages of computerisation if feelings of insecurity are to be avoided, and it may be that the kind of stress-related problems mentioned above can be reduced if workers are aware of, and in agreement with, the likely impact on their role from the outset and are actively involved in the whole process from feasibility to implementation.

A satisfactory resolution of the human issues should perhaps be the most important consideration of any organisation planning to introduce computers. The process will be much more successful and the systems will run much more smoothly if staff are committed to making it so.

References

Andrew J. (1987) *Computerising and the need for a training programme* Disse rtation submitted for BSc(Hons) in Quantity Surveying, Trent Polytechnic

Arthur C. (1987) 'Fraud inspires CBI to act' *Computer Weekly* 22/1/87

Atkin B. (1987) 'Computerising' *Chartered Quantity Surveyor* March 1987 p. 10

Barrett D. (1987a) 'Secrets sold for £45' *Computer Weekly* 26/3/87

Barrett D. (1987b) 'Head scratching stuff' *Computer Weekly* 24/9/87 p. 38

Brown J. (1987a) 'When it's more than a movie' *Computer Weekly* 14/5/87 p. 30

Brown J. (1987b) 'How to assess the impact of disasters' *Computer Weekly* 28/5/87 p. 31

Brown J. (1987c) 'Fleeing the grim reaper's grasp' *Computer Weekly* 4/6/87

Brown J. (1987d) 'Don't panic as disaster falls' *Computer Weekly* 18/6/87 p. 17

Brown J. (1987e) 'The best laid plans...' *Computer Weekly* 25/6/87 p. 30–31

Brown J. (1987f) 'Prevention – as good as a cure' *Computer Weekly* 16/7/87

Carter D.J. (1984) 'Who checks the software?' *Construction Computing* October 1984p. 32

CICA (1981) *Chartered Quantity Surveyors and the microcomputer* RICS

Clark S. (1987a) 'Pilot highlights human factors' *Computer Weekly* 7/5/87

Clark S. (1987b) 'Are you sitting comfortably?' *Computer Weekly* 1/10/87

Computer Weekly (1980) '80% of DP frauds result of 'pure opportunism" *Computer Weekly* 6/11/80

Donnelly F. (1986) 'Coping with chaos' *Infomatics* August 1986 pp. 26–28

DOC (1980) *Micros in construction* Design Office Consortium (now Construction Industry Computing Association)

Ernest-Jones T. (1987) 'Why network security needs tightening up' *Computer Weekly* 26/11/87 p. 11

Fraser G. (1987) 'Making a full recovery' *Infomatics* December 1987 pp. 51–52

Holdsworth I. (1987a) 'Working the system' *Computer Weekly* 23/7/87 p. 20

Holdsworth I. (1987b) 'Hackers' spree spans Europe' *Computer Weekly* 24/9/87 p. 9

Hunt G. (1982a) 'Micronotes: A question of verification' *Chartered Quantity Surveyor* March 1982 p. 235

Hunt G. (1982b) 'Micronotes: Halve labour costs – don't use computers' *Chartered Quantity Surveyor* April 1982 p. 275

Hunt G. (1987) 'Micronotes: Get in training' *Chartered Quantity Surveyor* February 1987 p. 12

Huws U. (1987) *The VDU worker's handbook* London Hazard Centre, 103 Borough Rd., London SE1

Kochanski M. (1986) 'Locking up the data' *Infomatics* August 1986 pp. 44–45

Lawrence J. (1986) 'Rent, buy, lease – a beginners guide' *Construction Computing* January 1986 p. 8

McTaggart T. (1986) 'Are your security measures up to scratch?' *Computer News* 13/11/86

Mulholland K.A. (1986) 'Finding the right software supplier' *Construction Computing* Winter 1986 pp. 15–16

Norman A.R.D. (1983) *Computer Insecurity* Chapman and Hall

Parrett K. & Stead D. 'Computers: who needs them?' (1986) *Construction Computing* Autumn 1986 pp. 34–41

Powell M. (1987) 'Training is all Greek to some' *Computer Weekly* 28/5/87

Winfield I. (1986) *Human resources and computing* Heinemann

4 Computers and the Law

Objectives

At the end of this chapter you should be able to:

- Outline some of the more important provisions of the principal legislation concerned with the use of computers in a commercial environment including:

    (i) copyright and similar forms of protection
    (ii) the Data Protection Act (1984)

- Discuss the rights and liabilities usually conferred upon the users of 'off the shelf' software packages.
- Discuss the liability for errors which might arise from the use of software packages whether bought 'off the shelf' or developed in-house.
- Discuss the general legal issues surrounding contracts for the purchase of computer hardware and software.

Introduction

This chapter is intended to provide an outline overview of some of the more important legal issues which concern the use of those computer systems likely to be used by a quantity surveyor. More detailed consideration of the issues raised will be found in the publications referenced in the text. The law concerning computers tends to vary from country to country and is constantly changing; these notes consider the situation as it currently applies in the United Kingdom at the time of writing (mid 1988).

The legal protection of computer software

The law concerning protection of computer software is very confused, essentially because most of the underlying legal principles were developed either to protect authors and artists from unauthorised copying of literary or artistic works (copyright) or alternatively to protect inventors against unfair exploitation of their inventions by others (patents). The advent of computer programs which might exist only as zones of magnetism on a tape or disk, or even worse within the body of a 'chip' was, of course, quite unforeseen and the application of existing copyright and patent law has therefore proved very difficult. To add to the confusion, although many countries include similar legal principles covering copyright and patents within their own legal systems, there have on occasion been significant variations in the ways in which those principles have been applied, thus ensuring that the same piece of software may receive different levels of protection in different parts of the world. This situation has become increasingly important as communication between computers across the world has become more commonplace.

In general terms Brett & Perry (1981) identify four areas of legal rights which might, in theory at least, be used to provide some protection against copying and the unauthorised use of software. The areas are given as patent law, copyright law, the law relating to 'trade secrets' and 'unfair competition', but Brett and Perry admit that, of these four possibilities, the two most likely areas are those relating to copyright and trade secrets. A good basic review of the relevant legal principles is given in Nicolle (1987).

Copyright

The law relating to copyright developed largely during the eighteenth century to protect the rights of authors against unauthorised copying following the widespread use of printing. The law has, at various times, been extended to cover other written material for example shorthand notes (Pitman v Hine (1884)), football pools coupons (Ladbroke v Hill (1964)) and railway timetables (Blacklock v Pearson (1915)). The present Acts also cover sound recordings, films and design drawings.

The current law is enshrined in the Copyright Act (1956), as amended by the Design Copyright Act (1968) and the Copyright (Computer Software) Amendment Act (1985), and provides protection both during the author's lifetime and for 50 years after death. Whilst, as Wilson (1981) points out, the Copyright Acts make no specific mention of tapes, punched cards or transient displays as being among the possible forms which a literary work might take, Brett & Perry (1981) argue that since the definition of literary work has been extended to cover shorthand code there would seem to be little doubt that, in principle at least, computer programs stored on punched card or paper tape would come within the definition although programs stored on magnetic media might pose a greater problem. Written descriptions of the programs, operating instructions, user manuals and similar documents will, of course, be covered by copyright legislation.

Many computer software authors and software supply companies have long been concerned about the apparent ease with which software 'pirates' have been able to circumvent what was perceived to be the spirit of the law. Losses to UK software companies caused by software piracy have been estimated to be as much as £150,000,000 per annum and an intensive campaign for more definitive legislation has been conducted by many interested parties, among the most active of which is an organisation of software suppliers known as the Federation Against Software Theft (FAST). The FAST initiative has apparently begun to have some effect; Nicolle (1988) reports on the computer industry reaction to the new Copyright Designs and Patents Bill presently passing through Parliament, and Nicolle (1987) reports on a number of successful prosecutions for software piracy. Ernest-Jones (1988) reports the first ever custodial sentence for software piracy passed on a software distributor in late 1987 after he was found guilty of forgery, copyright infringement, the illegal importation of software and offences against the Trades Descriptions Act.

Even if it can be assumed that copyright protection exists practical problems remain. One problem is that the intention of the copyright system is to protect the skill and care of the author in expressing a particular idea in literary form; there is no attempt, or wish, to provide protection for ideas themselves although as Wilson (1981) points out it is sometimes very difficult to draw the line between the two, and this might particularly apply in the case of computer software where one person might write a program using an algorithm developed by another which produces identical results but uses a different language.

A second problem is that of proof. Before a plaintiff can bring a successful action for breach of copyright he must prove that an infringement has actually occurred, and this can itself prove to be very difficult. By far the most widespread abuse of computer software is associated with the large-scale illegal copying of well known and well used 'industry standard' programs. Illegal copies are often made in the Far East and may well be provided to unsuspecting UK customers complete with professionally reproduced manuals in such a way that the total package is indistinguishable from the genuine article. Most major software authors however maintain a register of purchasers, and it is only when an unregistered owner of a pirated package contacts the software author for support advice that the real nature of the software becomes clear.

In law the user of pirated software could probably be sued by the copyright owner, but software suppliers have much more interest in catching the software pirate than in pursuing unwitting customers. One possible method which has apparently met with some success is reported in Nicolle (1988). In this case Ashton-Tate, authors of the dBase range of programs has offered all illegal users of their packages an immunity from prosecution and the right, for a small fee, to become legitimate and to receive future updates in return for naming the source of their programs. Such methods will plainly only work if users are aware that the version they are using is in fact illegal.

A further area of concern to computer users is the unauthorised copying and use of the data stored within a computer system rather than the programs themselves. Whilst Nicolle (1988) reports that data bases and programs created by artificial intelligence will be covered by the proposed new Copyright Designs and Patents Bill, the situation under present law is far from clear-cut, and in any event the burden of proof, particularly for files such as databases, may present a serious problem. It has been suggested that users might 'mark' their files with some 'dummy' information specifically to allow a positive identification in the event of proof of theft being required. The position with regard to data is also complicated by the fact that it was held in Oxford v Moss (1979) that pure 'information' does not fall within the definition of 'property' which may be subject to theft under the criminal law. Information alone therefore cannot be stolen.

Perhaps the best advice is to introduce and maintain suitable security systems to prevent the theft of such information in the first place.

Trade secrets

In addition to any rights of action under the copyright laws, rights of action may also apply under the law relating to trade secrets. This branch of the law is not primarily based in statute but is instead based on that principle of equity which attempts to protect relationships of confidence. The law will therefore act to prevent or restrict one party from taking unfair advantage of the relationship by preventing him from using confidential information in an improper way. In the words of Lord Denning, the law is essentially based on:

> ....the broad principle of equity that he who has received information in confidence shall not take unfair advantage of it. He must not use it to the prejudice of him who gave it without obtaining his consent.
>
> (Seager v Copydex (1967))

The Law Commission in 1974 recognised three factors to be considered in any particular case:

The nature of the information

The information must be confidential and must be seen to be so. The courts seem prepared to take a wide view; in the words of Megarry J:

If the circumstances are such that a reasonable man standing in the shoes of the recipient of the information would have realised that upon reasonable grounds the information was being given to him in confidence then this should suffice.

(Coco v A.N. Clark (Engineers) Ltd. (1969))

The relationship between the parties

It was established in Saltman Engineering v. Campbell Engineering Ltd. (1948) that a contractual relationship is not essential, although it was held in Lamb v. Evans (1893) that if a contract does exist it will be held to contain implied terms equivalent to the equitable obligation. Whilst the dictum of Lord Denning in Seager v. Copydex appears to imply a direct relationship of this kind, Wilson (1981) points out that in Prince Albert v. Strange (1849) the plaintiff was held to be entitled to an injunction against a third party who was the recipient of confidential information initially given by Prince Albert to another, and a similar decision was reached in Argyl v. Argyl (1969). The crucial point in these cases seems to be that the third party involved knew that the information was confidential and that he should not have had access to it, but consider the case of an employee who copies confidential information belonging to his employer and subsequently sells the information as his own to an innocent third party. Would the employer have a right of action against the third party?

Although such a scenario has yet to be specifically decided by an English court, in Seager v. Copydex (No. 2) (1969) the defendants were held to be liable even though they believed their product to be a result of their own development and not to be based on information obtained from the plaintiff. Despite this decision, it seems unlikely that a defendant could be accused of breach of trust if he had no knowledge that the information in question was confidential. Wilson (1981) points out that it has been accepted in the USA that once the third party has been made aware of the the confidence then he becomes bound by it and must not disclose the information to others. He may however be permitted to continue to use the information himself if he has substantially changed his position as a result of it, for example, if he has installed new plant in order to exploit it.

Misuse of the information

Any unauthorised use of confidential information for profit is a misuse. It is however for the plaintiff to prove that confidential information has been misused, either by the defendant directly or by some third party and this may be extremely difficult to do particularly in the case of computer software and data.

Remedies for breach of copyright or unauthorised use of confidential information

Breach of copyright is a criminal offence, and in addition a number of remedies are also available under the civil law.

The principal remedies in the case of computer software or data will be either an injunction, damages or an order for delivery up and destruction of the relevant documents, tapes, disks etc. The Court may also make an order for the preparation of an account of profits. Damages may be awarded and will normally be based on the market value of the information rather than the loss actually suffered by the plaintiff. The court however has considerable discretion in deciding the level of damages appropriate in each particular case.

The Data Protection Act (1984)

One particular kind of computerised information the confidentiality of which is often specifically protected by law is that from which an individual may be identified. Such information is regulated in the United Kingdom by the Data Protection Act (1984). The United Kingdom is not alone in this area, indeed one of the main reasons for the introduction of the Data Protection Act was to comply with the Council of Europe Data Protection Convention first opened for signature in 1981. The majority of European and Scandinavian countries either already have or are in the process of enacting similar legislation, and outside Europe legislation exists in the USA, Canada, Australia and New Zealand. It is typical of the British parliamentary process that the need for some form of protection for personal data was recognised as long ago as 1969, when Kenneth Baker introduced his Data Surveillance Bill in the House of Commons.

The prime purpose of the Data Protection Act is to regulate the storage and communication of personal information stored in computer systems. It does not relate to personal information stored or manipulated in any other form.

In principle the Act requires users of data (termed 'data users' in the Act) which might identify particular individuals (termed 'data subjects') and which is stored in computer systems for whatever purpose to register with a Government-appointed Data Protection Registrar. The Act allows certain exemptions from either the whole or parts of the Act for certain classes of data which do not pose a particular threat to the privacy of data subjects, or for data collected in connection with national security, the administration of justice, the detection of crime or for tax collection. In terms of normal business activity, data relating to payroll and pensions, and name and address files used only for distribution purposes are exempt from registration, and certain exemptions also apply to data stored purely for statistical or research purposes. The quantity of personal information covered by such exemptions is considerable, and the possible extent of uncontrolled access to such data has given grounds for concern; *Computer Weekly* (1988) reports on a motion in the House of Commons which claimed that MI5 can access information about any adult in the United Kingdom through the Department of Health and Social Security computer centre, that the electoral roll is used by police and immigration officials, can be sold to any organisation, and that such activities are not regulated by the Act.

All registrations made under the Act are required to give:

(i)   the name and address of the data user
(ii) a description of the personal data held
(iii) a statement of the purpose for which the data is held
(iv) a description of the sources of the data
(v)   persons to whom the data may be disclosed
(vi) countries to which the data may be sent
(vii) an address for receipt of requests from data subjects for access to the data

The register is maintained by the Registrar and is available for public examination. Failure to register, or to keep a registration up to date constitutes a criminal offence and will result in prosecution. The Registrar has a number of investigators under his direct control, and if he suspects a breach of the Act may seek access to a data user's premises. If access is denied then the Registrar may apply for a warrant empowering him to enter, search and seize discs, tapes, documents etc. Kavanagh (1987) reports the first ever such raid on the home of a Staffordshire special constable in October 1987.

The Registrar also has the power to refuse an application for registration, and data users who then continue to process the information commit a criminal offence.

Data subjects have the right to a copy of any personal data held by any data user covered by the Act, and data users are entitled to make a small charge to cover the processing costs involved. Data subjects also have the right to correction of incorrect or inaccurate data, and also a right to damages for any loss directly attributable to either the use of incorrect data or the loss or unauthorised disclosure of the information to third parties.

The Act is underpinned by eight 'data protection principles':

(i)   Personal data shall be obtained and processed fairly and lawfully
(ii)   Personal data shall be held only for one or more specified and lawful purposes.
(iii) Personal data held for any purpose shall not be used or disclosed in a manner incompatible with those purposes.
(iv)   Personal data held for any purpose shall be adequate, relevant and not excessive in relation to that purpose.
(v)   Personal data shall be accurate and, where necessary, kept up to date.
(vi)   Personal data held for any purpose shall not be kept for any longer than is necessary for that purpose.
(vii) Individuals shall be allowed rights of access to personal data.
(viii) Appropriate security measures shall be taken against unauthorised access, alteration, disclosure or destruction of personal data.

More detailed consideration of the Data Protection Act may be found in Savage & Edwards (1984) and Sterling (1984).

Contracts for the supply of computer systems

All of the normal rules of contract law governing offer, acceptance and consideration apply, of course, to contracts for computer systems, but there are a few additional pitfalls which might arise because of the typical quantity surveyor's lack of familiarity with the details of computer systems.

Sellors (1984) gives a good introduction to the problems inherent in the successful negotiation of contracts for computer systems, and Gooch (1986) includes detailed comment on the successful selection and purchase of computer systems for small contractors. The major potential problem areas which must be specifically addressed during the negotiation and contracting process have been identified by Bigelow & Nycum (1975) as:

Basic requirements

The actual functions which the system is required to perform must be defined in as much detail as possible. In particular requirements such as the required standards of accuracy, anticipated volumes and formats of input and output, acceptable timescales for each of the various processes, implementation period and training programme etc. must be specified as accurately as is reasonably possible. It is essential for all parties involved to have the the same expectations of system performance if future disagreements are to be avoided.

Responsibilities of the parties involved

All parties must be absolutely clear about their respective responsibilities. It is fundamentally important to the successful implementation of any computer system that the client, user, hardware supplier, software supplier, systems analyst and any other specialists involved understand their obligations and responsibilities to each other, and that these obligations and responsibilities are written down and mutually agreed. It is equally important that one party is responsible for managing and co-ordinating the whole process, and that all of the other parties recognise his authority.

System specifications for hardware and software

The system specifications must be settled before any contracts are signed. Details may be based upon some sort of performance specification, but in this case it is important to specify as precisely as possible the circumstances under which that optimum performance is to be achieved. Although this method of evaluation is widely used, for example for bill production systems, such systems are often purchased on the basis of their performance in one particular user's office, often the firm which developed the software in the first place. There is no guarantee that because a system performs adequately in one environment it will also do so in another; what is perfectly satisfactory to one office or firm may be quite unacceptable to another. It is equally important, particularly for systems which mix hardware from one supplier with software from another, to establish exactly who is responsible for ensuring that the system as a whole meets the specified criteria. Noise control may also be a problem, and maximum permissible levels should be stated where appropriate.

Site preparation

Ambient operating conditions for the equipment must be established as early as possible and arrangements must be made for the provision of any necessary air-conditioning, clean power supplies etc. Arrangements must also be made to acquire any necessary specialist furniture etc. required. Any necessary security precautions should also be implemented to ensure the integrity of the machine and the data.

Training

Particular attention should be paid to training, particularly who should be trained to administer the system, and who to use the system. The amount of training required and the cost must be established and included in the contract price.

Delivery, installation and acceptance

Detailed schedules of delivery dates must be agreed, together with responsibility for the installation and testing of the equipment. The contract must also include details of the tests which must be satisfied both by each component individually and also by the system as a whole before the system is accepted.

Financing

The time and method of payment must be agreed, including the cost of 'extras' such as additional training days, maintenance etc. Lawrence. (1986) gives a good introduction to possible financing options.

Maintenance

Establish the necessary maintenance procedures for both the hardware and the software (see chapter 3). Do not forget to make some provision to cater for catastrophic failure.

Modifications and upgrades

Contracts should include some provision for possible upgrades to either software or hardware or both. A system should be devised for reporting software faults, and a mechanism should also exist for notification by the supplier of known 'bugs' together with corrections as required.

Warranties

Warranties must be carefully detailed in the contract. Many manufacturers of small computers offer warranties as short as 40 days from the date of delivery, whereas suppliers may well extend the warranty period to 12 months. Pay particular attention to the warranties in the case of systems built up of equipment manufactured by a number of different firms, and ensure that someone provides an acceptable warranty on the system as a whole. Warranties on software may be especially restrictive, and this aspect is discussed in more detail below.

The purchase of computer software

It is important to recognise that, in most cases, the purchase of a software package does not confer any ownership of the software itself, merely a licence to use it. Most software packages purchased 'off the shelf' are supplied shrink-wrapped in plastic, often with the licence agreement prominently displayed, but sometimes there will only be a notice on the outside of the package stating that, by opening the package, the user accepts and becomes bound by the terms and conditions of the licence which are set out in full inside. Such licence agreements will attempt to limit things like the extent to which the software may be copied, the use of the software and the liability of the vendor in respect of errors.

The following clauses are not extracted from any particular licence agreement, but are typical of those which may be included in a package designed to run on a microcomputer.

> *You should read carefully the following terms and conditions before opening this package. By opening this sealed package you agree to become bound by all of the terms of this agreement. If you do not wish to become so bound then return this package unopened to your dealer for a full refund.*

This clause invariably appears either as the first clause of the agreement, usually printed in bold type in capital letters, or as a notice prominently displayed on the outside of the package. It attempts to establish the purchaser's acceptance of the licence agreement as an implied term in the contract of sale. There is, at present, considerable concern about the effectiveness of these so called 'shrink-wrapped' licences, and a number of lawyers have expressed doubt as to whether they could, in fact, be enforced. The question has not yet come before an English Court.

> *This software is licensed for use on a single computer (that is a computer with a single cpu) at a single location provided that you abide by the terms of this licence agreement. The software may be moved from one machine and physically transferred to another machine but shall not be used concurrently on more than one machine. If you wish to operate this software on a network then please contact the authors to arrange a site or multi-user licence.*

This clause establishes the licencee's right to use the software but only on a single computer. One of the major difficulties faced by users who wish to implement the same software package on a number of machines is that, under this provision of the licence agreement, a separate copy must be purchased for each machine. There is the provision for negotiation of a site or multi-user licence, but this is often not much cheaper than buying multiple copies of the software. Note also that the licence is only granted whilst the user abides by its terms, and the implication is that the licence is automatically revoked in the event of a breach.

This software and the accompanying written materials are the subject of copyright, and the copying of the software or of the written materials is strictly forbidden except as expressly provided herein. You may make one copy of the software solely for back-up purposes provided that the copyright notice is included on the back-up copy.

Copyright in the material is established, but note that the agreement does allow copying of the software but only for back-up purposes. Note that this provision will not be of any value if the original disk is copy-protected.

You may not transfer the licence to use software to anyone without the prior written consent of the copyright holder. Any authorised transferee shall agree to be bound by the terms of this agreement.

Software authors attempt to keep track of the authorised users of their packages by maintaining a register. The aim is to enable the users of 'pirated' software to be discovered, but the efficiency of this method must be very questionable.

This software and the accompanying written materials including the instructions for use are provided 'as is' without warranty of any kind. The authors do not warrant, guarantee or make any representation regarding the use, or fitness for purpose, or the accuracy of the results obtained from the use of the software. The entire risk as to the results or performance of the software is assumed by the licensee, and if the software is defective the licensee will take full responsibility for and assume the full cost of any repair or corrective action. Neither the authors nor anyone else involved in the creation, production or delivery of this product shall be liable for any direct, indirect, consequential or incidental damages arising from the use or abuse of this product.

The authors attempt to exclude themselves from any liability whatsoever. Note the attempt to make the customer liable not only for the consequences of the use of the software, but also for the consequences where the software is defective and even for remedying defects in the software itself! This provision could have extremely serious consequences particularly, for example, in the case of programs for structural design.

Fortunately, it is extremely doubtful whether such a clause would be upheld by a Court of Law.

Errors arising from the use of computer software

As illustrated above the authors and vendors of most off the shelf software packages attempt to severely limit their liability for the effects of 'bugs' in the product. There is presently considerable argument about whether or not software of this kind is governed by consumer protection legislation and, more important, the extent to which it is subject to the Sale of Goods Acts and the Consumer Protection Act (1988) (see Ernest-Jones (1987), Thomas (1987) and Arthur, Mehta & Ernest-Jones (1988)). The basic problem centres around whether or not the software can be classified as a 'product' within the terms of the Act. Whilst the physical medium upon which the program is written is undoubtedly a product, and is therefore covered, the same would not necessarily apply to the program itself. It is however important to note that the Act covers only personal injury and damage to private property; economic loss is not recoverable.

Both software purchasers and third parties may have a right of action in tort against the software author if it can be proved that the author was negligent. It is important to remember that, although in contract the doctrine of privity exists, there is no such obligation in tort. It was established in Donaghue v. Stevenson (1932) that a duty of care is owed to:

persons who are so closely and directly affected by my act that I ought reasonably to have them in contemplation.

It is therefore possible that even third party users of a software package could, in theory at least, sue the author for negligence if it can be shown that he had been negligent in the writing of the program. The practicalities of doing so would however be somewhat difficult.

Damages for loss of business property are available in negligence, and have in the past also been awarded for pure economic loss (e.g. Junior Books v. The Vietchi Co. Ltd (1982)). The Courts are however backtracking somewhat from the decision reached in Junior Books, and it is now unlikely that damages for pure economic loss would be awarded in negligence.

In the case of software written especially for a particular firm however, particularly if the contract for the system contained clauses such as those mentioned earlier (for example governing permissible standards of accuracy etc.), the situation is likely to be somewhat more straightforward. In this case it is likely that, although the user will carry the responsibility for the correctness of the computer's results, if he can show that the software is defective then he will have a right of action under the law of contract against the software author and may thus be able to 'step down' his responsibility.

Negligence

In general a specialist who contracts to provide some skill, for example carrying out a systems analysis or developing a computer program, is bound by the provisions of the Supply of Goods and Services Act (1982) which states that:

> In a contract for the supply of a service where the supplier is acting in the course of business, there is an implied term that the supplier will carry out the service with reasonable skill and care.

This actual meaning of this requirement was defined as long ago as 1957 as:

> Where you get a situation which involves the use of some special skill or competence, then the test as to whether there has been negligence or not is not the test of the man on the top of the Clapham omnibus, because he has not got this special skill. The test is the standard of the ordinary skilled man exercising and professing to have that special skill; it is well established law that it is sufficient if he exercises the ordinary skill of an ordinary competent man exercising that particular art.
>
> (Bolam v Friern Hospital Management Committee(1957))

In other words the court will basically expect that professionals will display the same standard of skill and care as might be expected from a reasonably skilled and competent professional using well practised and accepted professional methods of reaching a conclusion. Note that this does not imply that a professional person warrants the succesfull outcome of their endeavours, merely that they will exercise due care in seeking to obtain the desired result. For example, a doctor could not be sued for professional negligence following the death of a patient provided that his treatment of the illness was not at fault, similarly an architect undertaking the design of a building cannot be held liable in negligence if the client is dissatisfied provided that he can be shown to have exercised due care in formulating his design.

References

Arthur C., Mehta A. and Ernest-Jones T. (1988) 'Learning the facts of life' *Computer Weekly* 7.1.88 p. 18

Bigelow R.P. and Nycum S.H. (1975) *Your computer and the law* Prentice-Hall International

Brett H. & Perry L. (eds) (1981) *The legal protection of computer software* ESC Publishing

Computer Weekly (1988) 'Report by the Parliamentary Correspondent' *Computer Weekly* 7.1.88 p. 6

Ernest-Jones T. (1987) 'Software bugs can end in court' *Computer Weekly* 1.10.87 p. 3

Ernest-Jones T. (1988) 'Software pirate is first in gaol' *Computer Weekly* 14.1.88 p. 1

Gooch B. (1986) *The computer guide for builders* Privately published

Kavanagh J. (1987) 'Officers make first strike' *Computer Weekly* 29.10.87 p. 1

Lawrence J. (1986) 'Rent, buy, lease – a beginner's guide' *Construction Computing* January 1986 p. 8

Nicolle L. (1987) 'Softly softly through the law courts' *Computer Weekly* 2.7.87 p. 27

Nicolle L. (1988) 'Nations move in to rid software sea of piracy' *Computer Weekly* 21.1.88 pp. 20–21

Savage N. & Edwards C. (1984) *A Guide to the Data Protection Act 1984* Financial Training Publications Ltd

Sellers J. (1984) 'Contract negotiation' *Construction Computing* January 1984 pp. 29–31

Sterling J.A.L. (1984) *The Data Protection Act 1984 – a guide to the new legislation* CCH Editions Ltd

Thomas M. (1987) 'Protect the consumer – and yourself too' *Computer Weekly* 26.11.87 pp. 34–35

Wilson A. (1981) 'The protection of computer programs under Common Law – procedural aspects and United Kingdom copyright law and trade secrets' in Brett H. & Perry L. (eds.) *The legal protection of computer software* ESC Publishing

5 General Purpose Software

Objectives

At the end of this chapter you should be able to:

- Outline the advantages and disadvantages to be gained from the use of word processing systems, spreadsheets, simple database management software and integrated software packages.
- Explain the basic principles of operation of word processors, spreadsheets and database management systems.
- Discuss the ways in which quantity surveyors might use general purpose software.

General purpose software

In the beginning all computer software packages dealt with specific problems, for example a payroll program, a program to calculate the size of a steel beam or a program to process Bills of Quantity. Programs such as these are commonly written in one of the so-called 'higher level' computer languages such as COBOL or Fortran, and one's ability to use the computer to solve new problems using such methods obviously requires familiarity with a conventional programming language.

During the mid-1970s however the advent of small desk-top computers led to the development of interactive general purpose computer programs such as spreadsheets for the manipulation of mathematical data, word processors for the manipulation of text and data manipulation systems to allow information to be stored, classified, sorted and retrieved in accordance with user defined criteria. Such programs can obviously be used to solve a wide range of different problems, and such 'general purpose' packages have now been developed to the point where they offer very powerful tools to the computer user without the need for conventional programming skills. Collectively they probably now constitute the most widely used range of computer software.

They are in general extremely reliable and easy to learn. McDonagh and Daly (1987) gives an excellent account of the use of general purpose software packages in a private quantity surveying practice.

Word processors

Word processing essentially means the manipulation of written text by electronic means, and computer systems of this type are commonly used in modern offices. Because the use of computers permits the easy alteration and reorganisation of text stored in the system, word processors are obviously most useful for documents such as reports which may be subject to several revisions before the final version is approved. In the past this process often necessitated retyping the document after each revision, with the consequent risk of new typing errors occurring in a section of the report which had previously been 'clean'. The use of electronic word processing ensures that text can be easily inserted, deleted, altered or moved around within the body of a document, the current state of the document being always displayed on the screen and only printed out when all corrections have been completed.

Word processors may also be very useful for 'standard' documents such as standard letters or standard forms. In the past the use of 'standard' documents such as these meant the storage of large stocks of the pre-printed forms onto which names, addresses and other 'particular' information had to be typed, but the use of a word processor not only allows the standard text to be stored electronically and printed when required but also allows such documents to be 'personalised' very easily and very convincingly. The same techniques may also be used for other types of document for example specifications. In the past specifications were often prepared by 'cutting and pasting' a specification from a previous scheme and the draft was then completely retyped. Using electronic word processing documents can be 'cut and pasted' electronically and the need for retyping is virtually eliminated.

Types of word processor

There are essentially two approaches to electronic word processing:

    (a) word-processing software which will run on many types of general purpose office computer
    (b) dedicated word-processing computers where both the hardware and the software are dedicated solely to text processing

Whilst word-processing software for use on general pupose office computers has the advantage that the computer itself may be used for many other tasks, such systems may provide less sophisticated and comprehensive facilities than dedicated systems, although one must hasten to add that the software presently available is, in general, quite satisfactory for general office use. Dedicated word processors tend to be more expensive than a general purpose computer of equivalent power with word-processing software, but are likely to provide additional facilities such as customised keyboards with special keys for particular functions, and screens able to display a complete A4 page rather than the normal 24 lines × 80 characters commonly displayed on a normal VDU. In addition dedicated word processors may be capable of handling larger documents than can often be accommodated on a general purpose machine, and dedicated machines may therefore be preferred if large amounts of text are to be dealt with on a regular basis.

Basic elements of word processing

There are three basic groups of facilities which will be present in all word-processing systems:

(i)   Facilities for entering and editing text including the ability to move sections of text around within a document, copy text from one part of the document to another etc.

(ii) Facilities to control the appearance of the text on the page typically including control of margin widths, number of lines per page, text justification etc., and also a mechanism to allow the use of special printer facilities such as control of the type font, underlining, italics, sub and superscripting, bold face, line spacing, character pitch etc.

(iii) Facilities for storage and retrieval of standard blocks of text including the ability to merge into other documents as required.

The above facilities should be present in all modern systems but in addition particular systems might offer:

(i)   A spelling checker whereby the computer will check the spelling of all words in the document against a stored dictionary and will report any words not listed; the report will therefore include any mis-spelt words. Many systems allow correction dynamically during the spell-checking process, and some systems will even offer to correct unmatched words with close matches selected from the dictionary. Associated with the spelling checker there is, of course, a set of dictionary maintenance routines to allow updating as required, a most useful facility since most word-processing dictionaries seem to come with American spellings!

(ii) Automatic indexing facilities are normally provided only on the more expensive systems, but can be very useful in large documents.

(iii) A thesaurus facility to allow authors to ask the computer to suggest alternatives to particular words.

(iv) Automatic generation of tables of contents, usually combined with a system allowing automatic numbering of paragraphs in accordance with user defined criteria.

(v) 'Macro' facilities allowing commonly used sequences of keystrokes to be stored in the computer and invoked by the use of 'function' keys thus mimicking the single key-stroke facility usually offered by dedicated systems.

(vi) 'Mail-merge' facilities allowing complete runs of standard letters etc. to be printed automatically with specific information such as names and addresses being automatically inserted from another file as the letters are printed. The generation of such documents then becomes completely automatic once the operator has initiated the process.

(vii) Some systems offer limited mathematical facilities to allow, for example, columns of figures included in the document to be automatically summed.

Printers for word processing

The characteristics and methods of operation of those types of printer in common use have already been described in chapter 2, but the selection of an appropriate printer is obviously of crucial importance in a word processing context. Whilst suitable printers will almost always be included in dedicated systems, the choice of printer for word processing done on an office computer is much more difficult. Many organisations insist on 'typewriter quality' text for the final document, and have in the past been drawn towards printers of the 'daisy-wheel' type generating fully formed characters, but the main disadvantage of this type of device is the slow printing speed, typically no more than about 55 to 60 characters per second (cps). It has in the past been common to overcome this difficulty by using a second 'matrix' type printer operating at much higher speeds to produce the draft documents, using the daisy-wheel only to print the finished copy.

Small laser printers have recently begun to take over from daisy-wheel printers and offer an excellent alternative for those who require high quality print at high speeds. They are however rather more expensive than the other types of printer in common use, and cannot use continuous stationery.

Most modern matrix printers can operate in two separate modes, a fast (say 130 cps) draft mode and a much slower mode which involves multiple passes over the text to generate much higher quality print for finished documents. One such machine can therefore offer a useful compromise in a small institution if the budget is restricted.

'Social' effects of word processing

Perhaps the most important social effect which has typically followed from the development of word processors, particularly those implemented on portable lap-top computers has been an increasing tendency for executives to do much more of their own typing rather than either writing longhand or dictating either to a dictaphone or directly to a secretary.

In the words of Reis (1984):

Word processing is not just for secretaries. Anybody can use a word processor, in fact in my office we have no typewriters at all – everything is done on a word processor and we do most of the typing ourselves. One of the major advantages of word processing is that mistakes can be easily rectified; therefore bad typing is not a major problem. I find it quicker to word process myself than to dictate or write the stuff for a typist to type it out for me.

Other effects of the word-processing revolution may therefore be:

(a) not only to reduce the demand for pure typists but also to render those previously highly prized and accurate typists much less desirable than those who might be less accurate but faster
(b) to ensure that basic keyboard skills form an essential component of the budding executive's skills portfolio

Spreadsheets

Spreadsheets are to financial calculation what word processing is to text. Essentially, in its simplest form, a spreadsheet can be imagined as a large sheet of paper divided vertically into a number of columns and horizontally into a number of rows to form a grid. In the words of Hunt (1986):

(A spreadsheet) can best be described as an enormous electronic abstract sheet.

Each 'pigeon-hole' formed at the intersection of a column and a row is called a 'cell', and may be addressed by quoting the appropriate column and row numbers (see figure 5.1). Cells may contain either a number, some text or a formula indicating that the contents of the cell are to be derived by calculation from the contents of other cells.

	A	B	C	D
1				
2	apples	10		
3	pears	5		
4	total	(B2+B3)15		
5				

Figure 5.1

In figure 5.1 therefore:

cell A2 contains the text 'apples'
cell A3 contains the text 'pears'
cell A4 contains the text 'total'
cell B2 contains the number 10
cell B3 contains the number 5
cell B4 contains the formula B2+B3 to signify that the cell value is to be calculated by adding the contents of cells B2 and B3 giving a total value of 15

Spreadsheets provide a comprehensive range of in-built functions to allow extensive manipulation of mathematical data, and the facilities commonly provided may be grouped as follows:

(i) Text entry and editing functions including facilities to move or copy blocks of information from one part of the sheet to another. Since an electronic spreadsheet may be very large (perhaps dozens of columns and hundreds of rows), and a normal VDU can only display 24 lines × 80 characters of information, the screen is used as a 'window' which may be moved around the total spreadsheet at will. Most systems also allow the screen to be split either horizontally or vertically, or in some cases both, in order to display either two or four separate 'windows' at the same time.

(ii) Formatting functions to alter the display format of the sheet, for example some systems allow selected data to be displayed as bar charts, pie charts or histograms, to alter the widths of columns, to display information in alternative formats (e.g. integer form, truncated to two decimal places, scientific notation etc.).

(iii)Mathematical functions which may be included in formulae to allow the manipulation of data. Typical functions provided in all systems might include the following although some systems will provide many more:

+ addition
- subtraction
* multiplication
/ division
^ exponentiation (raising to a power)
< is less than
> is greater than
= is equal to
<> is not equal to
<= is less than or equal to
>= is greater than or equal to
SUM totals a list of numbers
COUNT counts the number of entries in a list
AVERAGE calculates the SUM of a list divided by the COUNT
MIN finds the lowest value in a list
MAX finds the highest value in a list
INT truncates a number to integer form
ABS removes any minus sign to give an absolute value
SQRT returns the square root of a number

In addition formulae may also include logical operators, for example if a cell contains the formula:

IF(expression,formula1,formula2)

then 'formula1' will be used if 'expression' is TRUE, whereas 'formula2' will be used if 'expression' is FALSE.
    Similarly the formula

OR(expression1,expression2)

returns a value of 1 if either 'expression1' or 'expression2' is TRUE, but returns a value of 0 otherwise, and the formula

AND(expression1,expression2)

returns 1 if both 'expression1' and 'expression2' are TRUE, otherwise a value of 0 is a returned.
    The formula

NOT(expression)

returns a value of 1 if 'expression' is FALSE or a value of 0 otherwise.
    These particular functions therefore provide the spreadsheet user with a branching mechanism, thus allowing spreadsheet packages to be used as

programming languages in their own right. Trigonometric functions are also commonly included (angles may have to be given in radians):

SIN(a) returns the sine of angle 'a'
COS(a) returns the cosine of angle 'a'
TAN(a) returns the tangent of angle 'a'

The ability to use formulae to derive cell values from the values of other cells obviously means that commonly used calculations can be set up on standard sheets and the results immediately displayed for any particular set of input data. Spreadsheet systems have thus achieved great success and widespread use among accountants and business planners for performing 'what-if' simulations, but it is a mistake to view them purely in this way. Weber (1987), in using a spreadsheet to create an expert system, draws attention to the wider possibilities:

> All too often spreadsheets are treated as if they were only fit for accounting and financial forecasting. Even the simplest spreadsheet is a limited form of language while the more sophisticated ones are powerful and versatile programming languages in their own right. Their control structures tend to be limited, but they do offer many advanced functions that would take a great deal of coding in other languages.

Spreadsheet systems therefore present extremely powerful and flexible tools for many different types of application. One or two systems even allow the data to be considered in a three-dimensional form rather than in the more conventional two-dimensional form, thus allowing the analogy of a book rather than a single sheet.

Typical applications which have been developed in quantity surveying include measurement (Smith (1986)), cash flow forecasting (Hunt(1986)), early design estimates (Williams (1987)) and the cost modelling of building services (Ellis (1986)). McDonagh & Daly (1987) record the use of spreadsheets for many aspects of quantity surveying work including cost planning, estimating and the production of interim valuations, and Cooke & Balakrishnan (1985) illustrate examples of use in cash flow forecasting, accounting, post contract management, life cycle costing and plane surveying. Hawkins & Massey (1985) also give, amongst others, examples of formula fluctuation calculations, 'ticksheet' valuations, cut and fill calculations, tender error correction and land valuation.

It seems possible that the spreadsheet concept will continue to develop even further. Ince (1988) reports that Xerox have developed a package called the Analytic Spreadsheet Package (ASP) within which cells can not only contain numbers, text and formulae but also 'objects' such as pictures, knowledge bases, dialogues, and pop-up menus.

Database management software

Perhaps the most widespread use of computers today, certainly in the commercial world, is for the storage and manipulation of information. The storage capacity of modern computer systems means that even small desk-top microcomputers can store, analyse and manipulate very large quantities of information, thus providing management with extremely powerful decision support tools. The use of databases as general purpose information systems by quantity surveyors in multi-disciplinary organisations is well established, but some have used small database manipulation packages in more specialised quantity surveying practice. The collection and manipulation of cost data is perhaps the most obvious area.

Betts (1987) proposes the use of a micro-based database package for the collection and analysis of information by building contractors for use during the tendering process.

The ability to store such large volumes of information poses a number of problems among the most pressing of which are:

(i) How does the user keep track of all of the information stored in the system?

(ii) How does the user instruct the system to select and present the information required in the form in which it is required for a specific purpose?

(iii) How does the computer manager ensure that the information is stored efficiently, can be accessed in a wide variety of ways and can be easily updated if required?

Relational databases

The problems mentioned above obviously become more acute the larger the collection of information becomes, and the administrative problems involved in controlling both access to and updating of the information become more difficult to satisfactorily resolve as the number of users increases. There is therefore the need to establish some logical structure within the computer, within which the information can be stored and which will allow the information to be referenced in such a way as to permit the scanning, selection, analysis and presentation of relevant information in accordance with particular criteria specified by the user.

Collections of data organised in this kind of structured way have become known as 'databases', and a wide variety of software tools have been designed specifically to organise and manipulate such databases, ranging from simple electronic 'card index' systems suitable for use on the smallest of microcomputers up to very large systems designed for use on large mainframe machines.

Information systems containing large volumes of data pose particular problems especially as regards organisation of the information. PMA Consultants (1979) is a useful study of the problems of controlling and integrating construction industry information, and also contains a good basic overview of the relevant principles of information science.

Such systems also present significant computing problems in order to ensure efficient storage of the information and optimum speed of access. Such problems become especially critical as the number of users grows and their reporting and presentation requirements become more complex, and some very complex methods of referencing the relationships between the various pieces of data have been devised. Databases organised on this kind of model are termed 'relational', and the definitive work in this area is encapsulated in a set of twelve rules formulated by Dr Edgar Codd. Codd's rules, summarised in Hares (1988), form an outline specification for a truly relational database. Hares (1988), however, points out that no available database management system yet complies with all Codd's rules although the technical solutions to ensure compliance are now well understood and it is likely that full compliance will be achieved very soon.

Infomatics (1988) contains a survey of available relational database management software packages, ranging in price from £400 for a system to run on an IBM PC up to systems costing in excess of £300,000 running on large mainframes. The most popular in the United Kingdom is shown to be the dBase III package from Ashton-Tate with a claimed 200 000 users.

Fourth generation languages (4GL)

One of the fundamental requirements for a good database management system is that the user should be able to interrogate the database in a language, similar to that used for natural speech. True natural language interaction with computers still remains a dream (but see also chapter 8), although considerable research has been carried out in this field. Each of the database management systems presently available includes some interpretation of a natural query language (indeed the language used for the Software AG product 'Adabas' is even called 'Natural'), and such programming languages have been termed 'fourth generation languages', often abbreviated to 4GL. Fourth generation languages as a class are very powerful and provide extremely clever ways of manipulating the information stored in the database with considerably less effort and within a much shorter time than was possible with languages such as COBOL or PL/1. Specialist programmers experienced in fourth generation languages are in great demand, and database query languages are now being used for many commercial application systems which would, in the past, have been written in languages such as COBOL. Reed (1987) is a case study of the problems faced by a major company who, with a need to update its commercial computer systems, decided to adopt a 4GL solution.

Database management and control

The introduction of a multi-user database poses particular management problems in that different users might need to be allowed different 'rights' to access and update the information. Information stored in a database is likely to represent a considerable investment in terms of time spent collecting it, and any organisation will naturally want to protect the database from unauthorised alteration by users whilst still allowing the data to be read. Alternatively, some parts of the data may be particularly sensitive, and one might need to restrict some users' access rights whilst still allowing access to other non-sensitive data. Most systems allow the data to be protected by various levels of security, and management must decide what database administration and security procedures are appropriate for each particular installation or organisation (see also chapter 3).

Integrated software packages

From the point of view of the microcomputer user, the three general purpose software tools so far described, word processors, spreadsheet systems and information management systems, form three complementary parts of a complete business system. In the past limitations on the available memory capacity have meant that it has only been possible to run one of the three packages at a time, and users have therefore been largely deprived of the facility to integrate information from one element, e.g. a spreadsheet, into another element, e.g. a word-processed report. The development of much larger microcomputers led directly to the development of software packages which integrated the three basic elements and attempted to provide facilities for the interchange of information between one element and another.

A number of such packages now exist, among the most popular are 'Symphony' from Lotus and 'Framework' from Ashton-Tate, but it should be noted that such packages are at best a compromise and are unlikely to provide the power of, for example, a dedicated database package such as dBase III.

Desk-top publishing

Desk-top publishing software is, in one way, a logical extension of word-processing in that it attempts to place facilities for the production of high quality printed material within the reach of the microcomputer user. Desk-top publishing is not however simply enhanced word processing; as Budgett (1987) explains:

> It is essential to recognise at the outset that desk-top publishing software is totally unlike any other; by itself it doesn't produce anything. It most closely resembles an infinite supply of blank sheets of paper onto which items may be attached in order to create a page, which may contain text or graphics or both.

Desk-top publishing software is therefore intended to allow users to emulate electronically the manual cut and paste operations involved in traditional publishing, as well as providing many alternative typefaces, styles and sizes of lettering. In essence it is to take the output from other programs, for example text created using a word processor, diagrams, charts and tables perhaps produced by a spreadsheet or business planning package, or even pictures created by a graphics design suite, and lay them out on to an A4 page so as to create a true camera-ready copy.

The process is therefore much more to do with art than technology; in practice a skilled professional paste-up artist can vary the layout to make the effect pleasing to the eye, informative, amusing or whatever other effect is appropriate to the particular work in hand. An understanding of the fundamentals of design and layout is therefore required if lay users are to make the best use of the facilities provided.

In practical terms any worthwhile desk-top publishing package will be able to read information in native format from a wide range of other packages and should be able to preserve attributes such as underlining, bold face etc., and should also permit text and graphics to be collected from different packages and merged onto the same page. Pictures read into a system using a scanning technique can also be reproduced but the amount of storage required to hold a reproduction of a black and white picture with sixteen levels of grey is enormous.

Systems are available to run on a wide variety of computers, but a laser printer is essential.

References

Betts M. (1987) 'A co-ordinated system of information retrieval for building contractors tendering' in Brandon P. (ed.) *Building Cost Modelling and Computers* E. & F.N. Spon
Brandon P. (1987) (ed.)*Building Cost Modelling and Computers* E.& F.N. Spon

Budgett H. (1987) 'What every desktop publisher should know' *Personal Computer World* August 1987 pp. 146–150

Cooke B. and Balakrishnan S.V. (1985) *Computer spreadsheet applications in building and surveying* Macmillan

Ellis C. (1986) 'M and E computer spreadsheets' *Chartered Quantity Surveyor* January 1986 pp. 10–11

Hares J. (1988) 'Tapping the trends' *Infomatics* February 1988 pp. 68–70

Hawkins P. and Massey R. (1985) *Spreadsheet examples* Trent Polytechnic Department of Surveying

Hunt G. (1986) 'Micronotes: The enormous abstract sheet' *Chartered Quantity Surveyor* February 1986 p. 15

Ince D. (1988) 'Defining The Object' *Infomatics* July 1988 pp. 66–71

Infomatics (1988) 'Survey of relational databases' *Infomatics* February 1988 pp. 74–78

McDonagh N.H. and Daly J.P. (1987) 'Cost management of construction projects' in Brandon P. (ed.) *Building Cost Modelling and Computers* E. & F.N. Spon

PMA Consultants (1979) *Relevance of information syntax to computer data structures* PSA Directorate of Architectural Services Data Co-ordination Branch

Reed D. (1987) 'Playing the fourth generation game' *Infomatics* October 1987 pp. 57–60

Reis G. (1984) 'All you wanted to know about word processing but were afraid to ask' *Construction Computing* April 1984 p. 4

Smith J. (1986) 'Measuring quantities with the aid of a computer spreadsheet' *Construction Computing* Autumn 1986 pp. 21–23

Weber J. (1987) 'Working to rule' *Personal Computer World* June 1987 pp. 130–133

Williams G.R. (1987) 'The development of a spreadsheet application for the cost modelling of buildings during the early design stages' in Brandon P.S. (ed.) *Building Cost Modelling and Computers* E. & F.N. Spon

6 Public Information Systems for Quantity Surveyors

Objectives

At the end of this chapter you should be able to:

- Explain what a bulletin board is.
- Explain what a public information system is.
- Outline the principal types of public information system which may be of use to quantity surveyors.
- Explain what is meant by 'public domain' software.
- Explain the hardware considerations which it may be necessary to take into account to allow access to bulletin boards and public information systems.
- Comment on the economics of using public information systems and the constraints which management might need to apply.

Bulletin boards

Despite the problems of communication mentioned earlier in chapter 3 computer systems have, for many years, been used to disseminate information. Groups of computer enthusiasts who may be spread over considerable distances have long been among the most active in this field, using their home computers to pass both programs, data files and messages via the public switched telephone network. Many of the early computer groups established a central data store which could be accessed by anyone else in the group, and which could be used to 'post' messages and notices of general interest. Such systems quickly became known as 'bulletin boards', and Toothill (1987a) states that the first such system was established in 1978 in the United States. The idea quickly spread, and in a very short time large numbers of open-access bulletin board systems became established, mainly among the computer hobbyist community on both sides of the Atlantic. Toothill (1987b) for example lists details of 130 such systems available in the United Kingdom in August 1987 including addresses and telephone numbers.

Electronic mail

A logical development of the early bulletin board services was the development of personal communication systems based on computers; essentially a system in which every user has his own private bulletin board onto which anyone with the correct telephone number and password can leave messages. In effect the system provides each user with an electronic mail box, and such systems have therefore become known as 'electronic mail', often abbreviated to 'Email'. The principal advantage of the technique is usually quoted as one of speed since the message is received so soon after transmission as to be almost instantaneous; devotees of the technique therefore frequently refer to the more traditional mail services as 'snail mail'. Many private organisations have their own electronic mail systems, often extending over considerable geographical distances.

The two best known publicly available electronic mail services in the UK are probably 'Prestel' and 'Telecom Gold'.

By far the largest and most dramatic growth in the area of electronic communication has been achieved by Fax (facsimile transmission) systems. The transmission side of a Fax machine essentially consists of an image scanner connected via a microprocessor to the telephone network. It can therefore scan and mail any image whether text or picture. Receipt of information is also controlled by the microprocessor, and reproduction of the image is usually by electrostatic means. Whilst the quality of drawn information is not particularly good at present the system is adequate for sketches and text. Nonetheless, Fax has revolutionised business communication in a very short space of time. The vast majority of firms now have a Fax machine, and it is possible for written and drawn information to be communicated almost instantly to many parts of the world. Improvements in the technology will doubtless mean that in the near future electronic communication of written and drawn information will become the norm and a reduction in the price of small machines will soon bring them within the reach of the domestic consumer. It is unlikely, however, that conventional postal systems will completely disappear. Fax is not at present suitable for documents larger than A4 or consisting of more than a few sheets, although no doubt even these restrictions will in time be overcome.

The EDICON initiative

Industries such as shipping already make considerable use of electronic mail, and probably the most important development in the use of the technology in the construction industry has been the establishment of an organisation called Electronic Data Interchange (Construction) Ltd, abbreviated to EDICON. EDICON was established in May 1987 as a nonprofit making organisation devoted to introducing electronic data transfer throughout the whole of the construction industry, and a full report was published in Stewart (1987). Working groups have been established to investigate the possibilities in CAD, bills of quantities production, ordering and invoicing and the production of technical and product information. Partners in the venture include, amongst others, the Department of the Environment Property Services Agency, construction groups Trafalgar House and John Laing, quantity surveyors, architects and leading materials suppliers and builders merchants.

The intention is to replace the majority of routine postal transactions with electronic data transfer within a period of five to ten years.

Public information systems

At the same time as the hobbyist community was establishing its open-access bulletin boards a number of private organisations were also developing similar systems for information dissemination either for use within individual companies or for particular restricted groups of people, and within a very short period of time it became apparent that information was a highly marketable commodity. Many such systems now exist, and many are available for general use upon payment of a subscription.

Some information systems, for example Ceefax and Oracle, are free of charge and do not even require a computer, merely a suitable television set, although conversation with such systems is of course a 'one-way' process and the system does not allow for any 'filtering' of the information by the user. Information is passed in 'pages', and the user must then select the parts required from the block of information presented.

The use of a computer to interrogate an information system means that the user can instruct the host system only to provide that part of the data in which he is specifically interested. The user is therefore able to search very large databases of information much more selectively.

A number of such systems exist which may be of direct use to quantity surveyors and which are generally available upon payment of the appropriate fee. Examples of such systems include:

- BCIS Online – Direct connection to the Building Cost Information Service.
- Textline and Infoline – Databases of news extracted from newspapers and magazines.
- Context – Information on building products, British Standards and Codes of Practice etc.
- BRIX - Building Research Station database including information on BRE Information Digests etc.

An example of a service which attempts to link the concepts of electronic mail, a bulletin board and an information system specifically for quantity surveyors is the TP-DOS Online system, an electronic mail and information service set up and run by the Department of Surveying, Trent Polytechnic. The system at present includes:

(i) A message area or bulletin board allowing users to communicate either with each other or to broadcast information to all users

(ii) A file area containing files of information, programs, details etc. which may be down-loaded to subscribers' machines

(iii) A services area allowing subscribers to remotely run software such as database enquiry systems which are resident on the host computer

The main disadvantage associated with the use of remote computer based information systems is seen by some as not the cost of subscription but rather the cost of connection. Even using the public telephone network however connection costs should not be too high provided that the host computer is within local dialling range. Even if the cost of the call were to be charged at the highest inland rate Toothill (1987c) calculates that the hourly connect charge should be only £10.17p (June 1987 prices).

Perhaps a greater disadvantage at present is that the whole business, at least in the United Kingdom, is still rather cumbersome and slow, but engineering improvements to the telephone network such as the installation of digital exchanges and fibre optic cables which are presently in hand should ease the problem in due course.

Public domain software

'Public domain' software is computer software which is readily available, usually free of charge, upon request. Users are allowed to copy the software, indeed are even encouraged to distribute it more widely, provided they do so without charge.

The idea of public domain software was born in the United States where a number of programmers, mostly hobbyists, decided that microcomputer software was generally too expensive and they therefore began to distribute their own programs free of charge. The idea has since grown, and Goodwin (1986) reported that in October 1986 the largest public software library in the United Kingdom, the Public Domain Software Interest Group (PDSIG) 'has a library of about 20 000 items on 1 200 disks.' All material is offered free to members of the library, upon payment of a small annual subscription. The various catalogues include all types of software including word processors, spreadsheet systems, data base managers, expert systems, computer aided instruction systems, communications packages and many more.

Programmers and software authors are not, generally, paid for software in the public domain, and whilst the range of public domain software is very large, the quality tends to be somewhat variable. In most cases the distribution diskette also includes program documentation and user manuals. The basic problem is that such software is not in any way supported and is offered 'as-is'. Users might therefore find bugs and problems for which there is no easy fix, but as Goodwin (1987) points out the same criticisms may be applied to a good deal of commercial software.

A variation on the public domain theme is 'shareware'. The shareware concept again originated in the United States, and is based upon the philosophy that most people will be prepared to pay something for good software. Accordingly the software is freely available, initially free of charge but users are asked to make a donation to the author of whatever they consider the software to be worth. Most authors undertake, upon payment of a stated minimum fee, to offer some degree of support including free updates to the software as and when they become available, and often access to a help line. Unfortunately the authors of most of the shareware available in the United Kingdom live in the United States and telephone help lines may not be all that useful!

A further twist is 'approval-ware'. This concept, common in the United States but so far uncommon in the United Kingdom, is very akin to the shareware concept described above, except that in this case users are in effect sent software 'on approval' through the public domain system. In this case users who decide to keep the software are asked to pay a stated sum of money as a licence fee. Similar incentives to those offered by shareware authors often apply.

Connection to a remote information system

Connecting a computer to a remote information system requires certain additional hardware and software. As far as the computer itself is concerned virtually any modern micro could be used provided that it has a serial (RS232) port. In theory all that should be necessary is to connect the computer to the host, install the necessary software and access the data base, but in practice, of course, nothing is that simple.

Unfortunately, the electrical signals generated by computer systems are not generally compatible with the electrical characteristics of the metal wires and exchange equipment of the normal telephone system, along which most long distance communications traffic is carried. It is therefore necessary to interpose some electronics between the computer circuitry and the telephone system in order to modulate the frequency of the signal to simulate voice traffic before transmission and demodulate the signal back to computer frequencies at the receiving machine. Such a device is called a 'modem' (MOdulator/DEModulator). In most installations the modem is external and plugged into the computer and the telephone system but internal modems are available for some machines. A particular form of the device which contains a special socket into which the handset of an ordinary telephone is placed is known as an 'acoustic coupler'. Such devices can be very useful for communicating from locations such as public call boxes where a direct jack-plug connection to the telephone system is not possible.

A schematic representation of the arrangement is shown in figure 6.1.

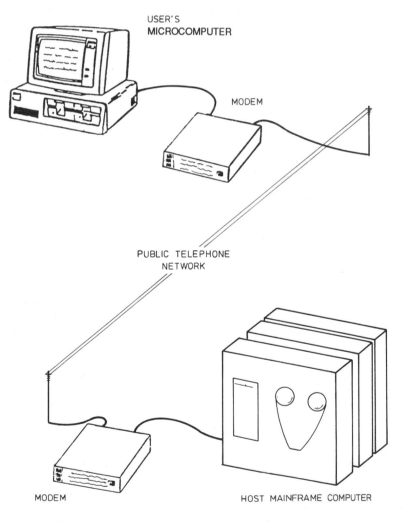

Figure 6.1 Connection to a remote information system

In addition, of course, users will need some suitable communications software to enable their computer to 'talk' to the host. Both of these requirements are discussed in more detail below.

Modems

In addition to converting the signal to a suitable frequency for the telephone system to handle, the modem usually also controls the speed of the transaction, and it is obvious that the modems at each end of the line must both be capable of operating at the same speed if meaningful communication is to take place. The speed of transmission is known as the 'baud rate', and most systems can send information in both directions at the same time; technically known as 'full duplex' operation. A number of different protocols exist:

V21   operates at 300 baud full duplex (approximately 30 per second in both directions simultaneously). This standard is now somewhat old fashioned and mainly used for acoustic couplers

V22   operates at 1200 baud full duplex, approximately 120 characters per second in both directions simultaneously. This standard is presently the most popular choice for communication over the public switched telephone system since it offers the fastest practical speed at which reliable communication can take place without complex error checking software. A wide variety of modems is available offering this standard

V23   operates at a split speed of 1200 baud in one direction and 75 baud in the other in full duplex mode. This standard is peculiarly British and was developed specifically for the Prestel electronic mail service. Equivalent character transmission speeds are about 120 characters per second in one direction and 7.5 characters per second in the other

V22bis2400 baud full duplex, approximately 240 characters per second in both direction simultaneously. Problems of line 'noise' become critical at speeds as high as this and complex error checking routines must be employed. Toothill (1987d) discusses the problem in more detail

Note that the above speed restrictions only apply because of the deficiencies of the telephone technology. Over short distances very much faster transmission speeds are commonly used; 9 600 baud full duplex (960 characters per second) is common with mainframe systems and speeds up to 19 200 baud full duplex (1 920 characters per second) are not unknown. In the future long distance communication speeds can be expected to increase dramatically with the widespread introduction of fibre optic cables and digital telephone exchanges.

Many modern modems also incorporate facilities to allow automatic dialling and answering (autodial/auto answer), and there are a number of ways in which such facilities can be controlled. The most common is a set of protocols developed by the Hayes company in the United States, and modems which use such a protocol are therefore designated 'Hayes compatible'.

Communications software

In order to actually use the computer and modem to transfer information the computer must be instructed how to transmit and receive data and to perform some system management functions such as logging the transactions. These functions are accomplished by a communications software package, and again there is a range of accepted protocols in common use. The most common in Britain are XMODEM and its derivatives and the Kermit program now available in the public domain. Toothill (1987d) gives a brief description of the protocols in common use.

References

Goodwin S. (1987) 'Computer answers "Free software" *Personal Computer World* October 1986 p. 206

Stewart A. (1987) 'Postage stamped out' *Building* 22/5/87

Toothill P. (1987a) 'News Bulletin' *Personal Computer World* May 1987 pp. 174–175

Toothill P. (1987b) 'UK Bulletin Boards' *Personal Computer World* August 1987 p. 214

Toothill P. (1987c) 'Go by the board' *Personal Computer World* June 1987 pp. 174–175

Toothill P. (1987d) 'Clearing the line' *Personal Computer World* April 1987 pp. 174–176

7 The Development of In-house Systems

Objectives

At the end of this chapter you should be able to:

- Explain the main factors to be considered when contemplating the development of an in-house computer program.
- Explain the basic principles of systems analysis in the context of the development of a new computer program.
- Outline the sequence of operations in the development of a new computer program.
- Explain the roles and responsibilities of the various professionals involved in the development of a new computer program.
- Discuss the management problems commonly posed by the development of new computer systems particularly in the control of time and cost.

In-house systems development

The development of purpose-built in-house software packages is a substantial task. It is invariably very expensive and hardly ever completed within the originally set parameters of time and cost. It should therefore generally only be considered as a last resort when all other options have been explored, but unfortunately this exploration process is often merely a cursory glance, and in many cases companies are discouraged by the apparent high prices of available software packages; there is always the feeling that it will be cheaper to do the job in- house using staff already on the payroll. In many cases this option, although it may appear at first glance to be more cost effective, proves to be a false economy. In the words of Gooding (1988):

> A great many companies look inside for solutions. They are still prepared to develop their own systems when a step back from the problem would tell them that reinventing the wheel is wasteful. Packages are more than

trouble free code; they represent an investment in someone else's experience.

In the event that it is decided to develop systems in-house, the actual development work is likely to be done by a professional systems analyst, but the major stumbling block which often occurs is that although the analyst knows a great deal about systems organisation and, usually, a great deal about the available computing options, he or she is much less likely to have a working knowledge of the client's business. This may pose particular problems in a specialist area such as quantity surveying where the technical jargon alone may be difficult for the analyst to understand, and it may take a considerable length of time before he or she is able to begin to build an accurate picture of the client's activities, to understand their particular special requirements.

On the other hand the typical client is equally unfamiliar with the systems analysis and design process. They know what it is they need to achieve, but are unable to articulate that requirement clearly in a language that the analyst can understand. In many cases this uncertain dialogue considerably lengthens the development process as both client and consultant gradually overcome this communications block. In the very worst cases both parties appear to have reached a consensus but, because of the communication problem, have differing perspectives of what has apparently been agreed with the result that the system, when it finally appears, is unsatisfactory. It is therefore possible for the client greatly to aid the development process and enable the analyst much more easily to reach a correct interpretation of their needs if the client too understands something of the process of analysis and systems development.

A further point to consider is that of the management of the development process. It is customary for the systems analyst to also act as development manager, but there is no reason why this should continue to be so. Indeed there is no more reason for the systems analyst to manage the development process than there is for the architect to manage the process of procuring a building. Many of the management techniques with which the quantity surveyor is already familiar are just as applicable to the development of a computer system as they are to the construction of a building or the installation of process plant.

This chapter then does not attempt to provide a comprehensive course on systems analysis and design, but rather to give an overview of the process from the layman's point of view.

The systems analyst

It is perhaps necessary, before beginning a discussion on the management of systems development, to establish what is meant by 'systems' and the 'systems analyst'.

NCC (1978:p. 1) defines a system as:

a set of interacting elements responding to inputs to produce outputs

Any system can therefore be considered as having three component parts: 'input(s)', some kind of 'process' and 'output(s)'. Examples of systems might therefore be the production of a Bill of Quantity, or the construction of a house. Both take some form of input, process it in some way and produce some output. Systems may in general therefore be represented as:

Input   —-> Process   —-> Output

The above definition, of course, allows some very complex systems. Indeed the whole of life could be seen as a system, and it is therefore common to break large systems down into component sub-systems, a process commonly known as 'factoring'. The system for the traditional production of a Bill of Quantity could therefore be seen, not as one system but as a collection of inter-connected sub-systems, for example taking off the dimensions, squaring, abstracting, billing, editing, typing and reproduction each of which is actually a system in its own right containing its own inputs, processes and outputs. Such sub-systems can therefore be arranged in a hierarchy to give a much more complete picture of the bill production process; the 'system' as a whole. It is the definition and analysis of such systems which is the primary task of the systems analyst. In the words of NCC (1978):

It should be clear that the major task of the systems analyst is to define the system in terms of its objectives, inputs, processes, outputs, boundary, and the interfaces between its subsystems.

The second task for the systems analyst is to understand how the the system behaves.

In the context of the above it is therefore obvious that systems analysis as a science, although it has in many minds become synonymous with computer applications, actually owes its origins to the management science techniques of operational research, the study of organisation and methods, and work study.

The system life-cycle

The actual process of systems development can be broken down into a number of discrete stages:

(i)   the preliminary assessment
(ii)   initial outline study
(iii) detailed study
(iv)   detailed systems design
(v)   programming
(vi)   implementation
(vii) maintenance and review.
        Note: Stages (i) – (iii) are sometimes collectively known as 'require-
        ments analysis'.

This collection of tasks is in many ways analogous to the tasks involved in procuring a building and is sometimes referred to as the 'system life cycle'. The process contains many natural break-points and feedback loops where management decisions are required and is shown diagrammatically in figure 7.1.

Note that, as in a building project, radical changes of direction become progressively more serious as the process proceeds.

Preliminary assessment

The preliminary assessment is a very high level overview of the proposed system. It will generally consist of an examination of the outlines of the problem. The objectives of the exercise are to set the bounds of the problem; to establish the terms of reference, and the outcome will usually take the form of a proposal for further investigation.

The process is largely investigative in nature and is in many ways analogous to setting the brief for a construction project. Although there may be advantages in this process being carried out by a trained systems analyst, the analyst can for example look at the problem from an unbiased viewpoint, the learning curve in the case of specialised areas like quantity surveying generally means that there is often much to be said for this process being carried out by a quantity surveyor provided that the necessary objectivity can be guaranteed.

At the completion of this stage the client has the opportunity to accept the proposal, to suggest possible revisions or to abandon the project altogether.

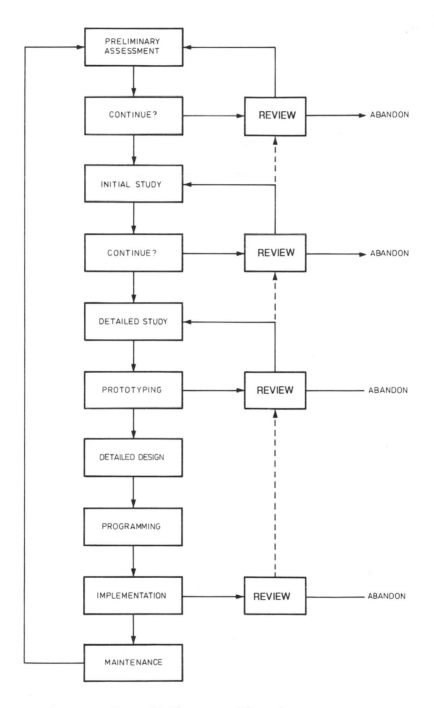

Figure 7.1 The system life cycle

The initial outline study

Working from the study proposal generated during the preliminary assessment phase the systems analyst will now begin an initial study of the problem. The study is likely to concentrate on an analysis of the existing system, inputs, outputs and processes in order that the analyst may formulate an understanding of the key areas and in turn develop an overall assessment of feasibility, time scale and cost. It is perhaps at this early stage that accurate communication between the analyst and the client is most important. It is at this stage that the analyst is likely to know least about the client's business; this stage where inaccurate perceptions of the problem may be formed; this stage where a complete understanding and common perception of the problem area is essential if the following stages are to be successful.

It is at this stage that the analyst is attempting to prepare the first tentative estimates of the scale of the problem, beginning to think about possible overall strategies and to prepare the first 'ball-park' estimates of cost. The analyst's job at this stage is to some degree akin to that of a quantity surveyor faced with a client who knows that their existing accommodation is inadequate but is unsure about whether to extend, refurbish or rebuild on a new site.

The outcome of the process should be a report detailing the analyst's perception of the problem including approximately costed alternative proposals together with projected time-scales and a note of the advantages and disadvantages of each. It is vitally important that this report should be written in a language and style that the client can understand, as it is on the basis of this report that the client will decide whether or not to invest substantial sums of money.

Once again the outcome will be either a decision to continue, to review and revise, which may also at this stage involve a reappraisal of the original problem assessment, or to abandon the project altogether. Total expenditure to this point is likely to still be relatively small and abandonment is therefore still a practical proposition. Beyond this point costs begin to rise steeply and the financial consequences of abandonment become progressively more serious. In the words of Davis (1983:p. 10):

> This presentation marks a crucial decision point in the life of the project. Many projects will die right here; only those promising a sufficient return on investment should be pursued.

A good example of the kind of problems which can occur when the early stages are not successful is reported in Ernest-Jones (1988).

The detailed study

Following successful completion of the outline study phase the analyst will now proceed to a detailed study of the problem and will attempt to prepare firm proposals for the system with more accurate estimates of time and cost.

There is a considerable degree of overlap between the detailed study and the detailed design phase, with no hard and fast rules about which phase certain processes fall into. I prefer for example to consider the detailed formulation of input and output mechanisms as a part of the detailed study phase, whereas other commentators (e.g. NCC (1978)) consider this to be part of the systems design phase. Nonetheless, the detailed study process is largely analogous to the sketch planning stage of a building contract with the analyst combining the roles of architect and quantity surveyor.

It is at this stage that the detailed 'systems analysis', or analysis of the customer's business is carried out. It is not the purpose of this text to give a detailed explanation of systems analysis techniques, but NCC (1978), Davis (1983) and Rothery, Mullally and Byrne (1976) all provide very readable introductions to the subject.

It is also at this stage that the most contentious decisions may have to be taken. Many laymen might see the function of the systems analyst as being merely to computerise existing manual processes, but this may be very far from the truth. NCC (1978:p. 33) says:

> The systems analyst is concerned with analysing systems with a view to making them more effective either by modification or by substantial redesign.

and later, p. 43:

> The systems analyst is an agent of change...

The systems analysis is likely to be much more concerned with the input to a system and the output from it rather than the manual process linking the two. It is therefore highly likely that the analyst may propose alternative and more economical ways of accomplishing the particular process, and this may have a very significant effect on existing jobs, techniques and work practices and hence upon the degree of acceptance of the final system by the end user.

As an example, imagine that one were to ask a systems analyst to investigate the bill production process with a view to maximising the efficiency of the use of computers and bearing in mind possible future links with computer aided design systems. The result of such an analysis might well be a system which might work by constructing a mathematical model of the building inside the computer from which the computer itself could measure its own quantities. Such a system would obviously require a totally different approach to measurement than has been conventionally used in the past; it might for example require the quantity surveyor to measure and input to the computer all of the measurements for the building on a wall-by-wall basis rather than by using the more conventional 'girthing' and elemental measurement techniques commonly used at present. Such a system might be extremely efficient, but would the changes to established practice be readily accepted by the rank and file of the profession among whom more traditional techniques are ingrained? One must therefore look very carefully at radical solutions, bearing in mind always that any new system requires the wholehearted support of its users if it is to be successful.

The detailed study process is essentially an iterative one requiring considerable discussion between the client and consultant. It can be a process in which the lay client feels most uncomfortable perhaps because he has considerable difficulty in visualising how the analyst's promised vision of the future will eventually appear. Such problems, if not tackled as they arise, may only surface when the finished system is unveiled and the clients reaction is 'Oh dear I didn't think it would be like that!' It is in an attempt to overcome this problem that some commentators recommend that 'prototypes' or 'mock-ups' of the user interfaces should be constructed during this stage of the work. Clients can then be shown proposed screen displays, output and report formats as the design progresses and can comment as required. The use of techniques such as this can be very helpful in that they enable the client to feel 'in-touch' with the project and a part of the project team. The use of prototyping as a technique is discussed in Ince (1988a), and some of the major problems are summarised in Ince (1988b). Ince (1987a) discusses the management problems inherent in the use of the approach.

The result of the detailed analysis phase will be a report detailing one or more firm system proposals, each complete with forecasts of time and cost. Davis (1983:p. 12) writes that the analyst may be asked to consider, as a minimum:

(1)   A low cost option which does the job and nothing more.
(2)   An intermediate cost solution that does the job well, and is convenient for the user. This system may include several features that the user did not specifically request, but that the analyst, based upon experience and knowledge, knows will prove valuable.
(3)   A high cost 'Cadillac' system, with everything the user could possibly want.

In the final analysis the decision again rests with the client whether to continue or to abandon the project. If the decision is taken to continue then one of the alternatives will be selected and this conceptual model will form the blueprint for the physical system.

In practical terms completion of this stage represents the latest point for the incorporation of major variations to the philosophy of the system. Major structural changes beyond this point will have disastrous effects upon the project in terms of time and cost overruns. It is therefore essential for the philosophy of the system to be fully and finally agreed before proceeding to the next stage of detailed systems design.

Detailed systems design

Once the detailed study is complete and the system proposal is agreed then work may begin on the detailed systems design. As mentioned earlier some commentators prefer to consider this phase as partly creative, but I prefer to consider the design process to be essentially a technical one concerned with the design of files, various computer processes, the detailed selection of equipment etc. The detailed design stage is therefore analogous to the 'working drawings' stage of a construction project; it resolves the technical problems inherent in converting the conceptual design into a physical reality. The output from this stage is therefore a complete design for all aspects of the proposed system which can then be passed to a programmer for conversion into a computer language.

It may still be possible to accommodate minor variations during the systems design phase but usually, as in a building project, only at the expense of additional time and cost.

Programming

Upon completion of the detailed design phase, or perhaps with some large systems overlapping with it, comes the process of converting the analyst's paper design into a working system; it is therefore analogous to the construction stage of a building project. The choice of programming language will already have been made by the analyst and the programming task is almost entirely a technical one.

In the early days of computing, programming was considered to be essentially creative. Tiny amounts of memory, extremely slow processors and very limited backing storage meant that considerable time and effort were expended in devising ingenious ways to use the computer most efficiently. Early system design techniques also left much to be desired, and tended to mean that much of the design was done by the programmer himself on a trial and error basis, with the result that programming was a very hit and miss affair with many changes of direction. Such systems thus tended to be extremely difficult to follow, were usually poorly documented and were consequently a nightmare to subsequently maintain.

Today however there is less of a need for 'clever' programming of this kind. The cost of hardware is now so low compared with software development cost that, with very few exceptions, complex and ingenious programs are regarded as a distinct liability. Improved system design techniques also contribute to better prepared systems and programming today is therefore no longer the uncertain process of only a few years ago.

Large systems will usually be constructed from a large number of sub-programs or 'sub-routines' each of which is written and tested individually by the programmer before being incorporated into the system as a whole. Unfortunately testing has, in the past, tended not to be one of the high profile activities of software development. Ince (1988c), in a discussion of automated testing methodologies, writes:

> Testing is the Cinderella of the software project. Whilst text-books and theoreticians place a large amount of stress on front-end activities, such as specification and design, those activities traditionally associated with testing have been ignored.

This is plainly unsatisfactory.

Upon completion of the programming stage the whole system will be tested by the analyst using test data usually supplied by the client in order to confirm that the system as a whole meets the originally agreed specification. Only when the analyst is completely satisfied that the program performs correctly in accordance with the agreed design criteria will he present the system to the client for implementation.

The effect of any variations at this stage will inevitably lead to major time delays and cost increases. In all but the most minor cases variations are likely to mean that the programming stage is abandoned in order that the analyst may reconsider the system design.

Whilst the programmer is actually writing and testing the individual programs the analyst will usually be writing up the detailed system documentation. Accurate and complete documentation is of course essential to ensure ease of maintenance and possible future upgrading.

Completion of the programming stage should therefore result in a complete working and fully documented system.

Implementation

In a perfect world implementation of a new system would simply be a matter of switching on the machine and handing the user an operations manual. In practice of course it doesn't work out that way, and there are inevitably snags which will require to be resolved before the system settles down, staff become familiar with it and the process begins to run smoothly. The management problems associated with introducing new systems have already been documented in chapter 3.

The ease with which a new system is implemented is a direct reflection of:

(i) the level of commonality and true agreement reached by the analyst and the client during the requirements analysis phase,

(ii) the skill displayed by the analyst in translating the agreed require ment into a working system and

(iii) the level of management expertise employed during the design and implementation stages

As noted earlier, it is in the first of these that the analogy with a construction project begins to break down. Construction projects are three-dimensional things which can be physically represented both on paper as architectural and artistic drawings, and in three dimensions by models. It is therefore comparatively easy to see whether the designer has correctly interpreted the client's brief. In contrast, computer programs are intangible ethereal things, and it is only at this final stage that the accuracy of the initial requirements analysis is eventually revealed.

Maintenance and review

The final stage in the system life cycle is the maintenance and review phase. Even if the previous phases have been completely successful and no amendments are required at initial implementation, most computer systems will need modification at some stage during their life, perhaps because of changes in legislation, for example a payroll system, or because of changes in methods of working, for example the introduction of a new Standard Method of Measurement.

Typically, most well designed systems can cater for some amount of change provided that the change does not strike at the basic philosophy of the system itself, but there will eventually come a point at which the extent of the changes, or the cumulative effect of a number of changes carried out over a period of time mean that a redefinition of the problem is required and the system life cycle must therefore begin again. The critical management activity must be in recognising when this point occurs; it is very easy to fall into a position where continued maintenance of an outdated and over-complex system imposes an ever-increasing main-tenance burden and yet the very high level of investment in the system deters management from throwing it away and beginning anew. A good example has to be the case of the British air traffic control system reported in *Computer Weekly* (1987). The article reports that because of a large number of computer system failures the existing thirteen-year-old system was to be replaced but:

> The Civil Aviation Authority is already committed to spending £200m refurbishing the West Drayton control centre and a new computer will be the biggest single item on the shopping list, but the software is so unwieldy that it is unlikely to be replaced. Independent experts are to examine the million lines of code which make up the air traffic control system ... The colossal investment means they will have to find something seriously wrong with the software before CAA decides to chuck it out of West Drayton. Starting from scratch is not an attractive idea.

Management of the development process

Bell (1987) and Neale (1987) both point out that, although software is an intangible thing, the management of software projects is not really that different from the management of any other project be it the construction of a building, building a ship or planning a production line. In essence the same management tasks apply; those of planning and controlling the use of the available resources in order to achieve successful completion of the project within the originally agreed parameters of time, cost and quality. It would therefore follow that the kind of management techniques used in other industries would be likely to be equally applicable to the development of computer software.

We should therefore consider:

(i)   forecasting of time and cost
(ii)   economic justification
(iii)   monitoring techniques

Forecasting of time and cost

Initial forecasting of time (and cost) is even more difficult for a computer system than it is in the early stages of a building project. Bell (1987:p. 76) reports that:

> Error factors of 200 per cent or 300 per cent are not unknown and worse figures are known.

Historically, managers have either based their estimates of time on previous projects or have used some form of formula. The use of previous project data requires an initial appraisal of the scheme to be completed, together with an outline assessment of the various tasks to be completed. Data from previous jobs is then applied and cost, resource and time forecasts are produced. Ince (1987b) calls this the 'pragmatic method', and it is of course very similar to the historical cost approach for early estimates of building cost. This approach has in some cases been computerised and systems have been built to automatically generate time scales for new projects based on such historical information. Ince (1987b) reports on the use of such a tool, called Cocomo, developed in the United States.

Alternative estimating methods use formulae of one sort or another. One example, the use of which is reported in Ince (1987b), is called 'Function Point Analysis' and was originally developed at IBM in the late 1970s. The method works by measuring the proposed system in terms of the functions required; the number of inputs, outputs, enquiry types, master files and interfaces required in the complete system. Each total is then given a weighting and a formula applied and the resultant number gives an indication of the time a new project will take. It is then a simple matter to combine the time with existing known staff costs to calculate the total estimated cost of the project.

Computer software development also has other parallels with the construction industry in that any time or cost figure given to the client, no matter how sketchy the information and no matter how approximate the figure, automatically becomes the maximum allowable and no matter how accurate subsequent predictions are the first figure given is the only one which will be remembered as if engraved on a tablet of stone! It is therefore essential that a sufficient contingency sum is allowed to take account of problems which might arise.

Bell (1987:p. 44) gives the following list of possible problem areas and suggests that the more items from the list that apply to the project the greater the chance that the project will not proceed as forecast:

(i)   Large team involved.
(ii)   Long time scale.
(iii)   Need to sub-contract.
(iv)   New skills required.
(v)   Senior management commitment unknown.
(vi)   Users not experienced in system projects.
(vii)   Large change in the user area.
(viii) Several distinct users involved.
(ix)   Change in users' power position.
(x)   New computer equipment.
(xi)   New terminals or communications required.
(xii)   New operating system.
(xiii) New language or environment.
(xiv)   Several equipment suppliers involved.

Economic justification

The development of a new computer system must be looked upon as an investment, and will normally need to be justified by the use of normal investment appraisal criteria. It is not within the scope of this work to give detailed explanations of investment appraisal techniques, but Bell (1987) gives examples showing the use of payback analysis, break-even analysis, net present value and internal rate of return. The economic justification of projects using techniques of this kind is usually a crucial factor in management's decision to abort or proceed.

Monitoring techniques

The successful completion of software development projects requires just as much carefully planning and monitoring as the construction of a building, and has historically used many of the same tools including bar or Gantt charts and the many different kinds of network planning in common use in construction. Neale (1987) however points out that the use of such techniques has not been entirely successful. As a response to the apparent failure of more traditional tools the software industry has introduced the concept of the Integrated Project Support Environment (IPSE) which attempts to provide a computer system which will itself aid the planning and monitoring of software projects. The concept is still very new and available systems are thin on the ground although Jones (1988) reports on the use of two systems available in the United Kingdom.

References

Bell R. (1987) *Management of systems development* Hutchinson
Computer Weekly (1987) 'Failures force Hobson's choice' *Computer Weekly* 20.8.87 pp. 14–15
Davis W.S. (1983) *Systems analysis and design – a structured approach* Addison-Wesley
Ernest-Jones T. (1988) 'Learning the hard way about fourth generation' *Computer Weekly* 7.4.88 p. 16
Gooding C. (1988) 'Time for the proof of the pudding' *Computer Weekly* 18.2.88 pp. 26–27
Ince D. (1987a) 'Model answers' *Infomatics* September 1987 pp. 61–62
Ince D. (1987b) 'Projecting the future' *Infomatics* October 1987 pp. 49–50
Ince D. (1988a) *Software prototyping in the Eighties* Privately published by the author at 39 High St., Greens Norton, Northants
Ince D. (1988b) 'Moving on from the middle ages' *Computer Weekly* 11.2.88 p. 32
Ince D. (1988c) 'Putting software to the test' *Infomatics* March 1988 pp. 52–53
Jones K. (1988) 'IPSEs start to come into their own' *Computer Weekly* 4.2.88 pp. 24–25
NCC (1978) *Introducing systems analysis and design* NCC Publications
Neale A. (1987) 'Managing "intangible" projects' *.EXE Magazine* November 1987 pp. 4–10
Rothery B., Mullally A. and Byrne B. (1976) *The art of systems analysis* Business Books Ltd.

8 Expert Systems – the Future?

Objectives

At the end of this chapter you will be able to:

- Explain what is meant by 'artificial intelligence'.
- Explain the meaning of the terms 'decision support system' and 'expert system'.
- Explain the various terms used to describe different sorts of expert system.
- Discuss the various kinds of problems which expert systems can help to resolve.
- Discuss the application of expert systems to quantity surveying, the construction industry and the related professions.
- Discuss the advantages and limitations of the use of expert systems.

Decision support systems

During the late 1960s and early 1970s a number of factors came together to radically change the way in which computers were used in business and commerce.

In terms of the computer hardware, interactive terminal-driven systems were becoming the norm, and mainframe computers had grown very large indeed with the capacity to store and manipulate vast quantities of information. Minicomputers were also well established both as stand-alone machines in smaller companies and also as front-end processors to larger and more complex mainframe machines. The microcomputer, although still regarded as a hobbyist's toy, had also begun to appear as a direct spin-off from the space race of the 1960s. The dramatic increases in both commercial computer usage and available computer power meant that virtually limitless quantities of information could be stored, and the use of terminal meant that the whole of that information could be made available to executives and managers at the touch of a button in the shape of a so-called computerised Management Information System (MIS).

The only problem in this corporate garden of Eden was the surfeit of information, all of which the executive decision makers were expected to absorb, evaluate, analyse and incorporate into their decision-making process, an excess of data which most managers found very hard to cope with. Keen and Scott-Morton (1978:p3) wrote:

> During this period the utopian dream (in retrospect, perhaps demonic would be a better term) of the total integrated database emerged. For example, some organisations aimed at storing all the company's data in a huge set of files, that could be accessed through a computer. This 'data centred' approach, carried to such an extreme, was neither useful nor feasible.

In short, management was in danger of being totally swamped by the information revolution; the dilemma is well documented by, among others, Dearden (1966), Nolan and Gibson (1974) and Kanter (1977).

During the same period a number of management scientists and behavioural psychologists were involved in studying the process of human decision making, a field of study which developed models attempting to both explain and assist the human decision making processs. These models eventually impacted strongly on both operational research and management science.

From the synthesis of these models and the enhanced information storage and recall facilities offered by the new generation of computers sprang the concept of a computer based Decision Support System (DSS). Such systems would no longer be simply huge information stores which overwhelmed the manager with both vital and useless information with equal zeal, but computer systems which would be specifically developed to allow the available information to be filtered so that the computer could actually assist the decision-making process.

Keen and Scott-Morton, building on the work of Anthony (1965) and Simon (1960), show that all management tasks may be defined as either 'structured' (e.g. linear programming of a construction project), 'semi-structured' (e.g. the preparation of an early estimate from very sketchy information), or 'unstructured' (e.g. hiring staff). Note that the taxonomy makes no implied judgement about the degree of 'difficulty' involved in each type of task, merely about the level of 'human intuition' which must be applied and thus, by implication, the presence or lack of 'rules' or models upon which to base a decision. Obviously the more highly structured a task becomes the greater the likelihood that a computer system could be developed which would follow the rules; hence computer systems should be able to replace managers only in those areas where the task is highly structured. A good example might be the day-to-day running of a complex manufacturing plant which used to be considered a difficult and challenging management task but is now commonly controlled completely by computers.

It is therefore in the areas of semi-structured decision making that the use of a computer based decision support system may perhaps be of the greatest benefit. Decision support systems therefore concentrate on aiding the decision maker in tasks where managerial judgement is still an essential element.

Moore and Chang (1983) point out that, in essence, virtually any computer system which aids decision making could qualify as a decision support system. Decision support systems might therefore range from, for example a spreadsheet model allowing 'what if' simulation to complex information bases allowing selection of information on the basis of user supplied criteria. They do however go on to propose a taxonomy which attempts to place decision support systems in context with other computer systems. They provide the following definitions:

Transaction Processing Systems (TPS) – pure data processing for gathering, updating and posting information according to pre-defined procedures. The TPS therefore involves no management decision making since most decisions are clerical and routine.

Management Information Systems (MIS) – systems with pre-defined data aggregation and reporting capabilities. MIS reports are usually either printed in batch or queried on demand. However if present, query options normally include only a set of pre-defined data extraction operators. The BCIS 'On-line' system might therefore be classified as a management information system.

Decision Support Systems (DSS) – extensible systems with intrinsic capability to support *ad hoc* data extraction, analysis, consolidation and reduction as well as decision modelling activities.

Keen and Scott-Morton (1978) give a number of examples of working decision support systems, and Bennet (1983) details the factors to be taken into consideration in creating new systems.

Some researchers, for example Gorry and Krumland (1983) have argued that decision support systems should take more advantage of research into artificial intelligence in order to promote the use of decision support systems as consultants to the decision maker rather than merely as passive information providers. Such research leads directly to one facet of what have become known colloquially as 'expert systems'.

Artificial intelligence

The concept of 'artificial intelligence', the construction of an 'intelligent' machine, is a subject which has captured the hearts and minds of men for hundreds of years. In the main of course, such things lie in the realm of science fiction, but in the years since the end of the second world war the pursuit of 'artificial intelligence', AI for short, using computers has become a widely researched area of study.

In order to make any sense of the concept it is first necessary to define what 'intelligence' actually is. Typical dictionary definitions speak of 'quickness of understanding', 'intellect', 'capability for rational thought' etc.; words which even given the most liberal of meanings could not be applied to any computer system yet in existence or even foreseeable in the near future. Despite the fact then that a considerable body of so-called artificial intelligence research now exists, the word intelligence, in this context, generally implies nothing more than an ability in some sense to 'learn'; that is to say that the computer system is able to evaluate the results of its own actions, and to modify its own behaviour in order to ensure that incorrect or invalid actions or responses are not repeated. Simple examples might for instance include a computer controlled industrial robot equipped with impact sensors which is required to perform some sequence of operations in a factory. Such a device could be made to modify its own behaviour pattern by taking input from the sensors whenever contact was made with some adjacent object, and using that information could construct a 'map' of its surroundings in order to prevent accidental collisions. The machine can thus be said to have 'learned' from its own experience; in some limited sense to have displayed some intelligence. Another example might be a computerised version of the guessing game 'Animal, vegetable, mineral', where the computer attempts, on the basis of answers to questions asked, to deduce the identity of some object, animal, plant etc. by means of a decision tree. In the event of an incorrect guess the system can 'learn' by asking how it could discriminate between the incorrect guess and the correct answer, and the new information is then added to the computer's internal decision tree.

Such examples are trivial and yet they do indicate the extremely wide range of artificial intelligence research. Many of the problems associated with the expansion of artificial intelligence are technical rather then theoretical, and are concerned with the simulation of senses which we take for granted. The construction of manipulative robots with the range of movement and delicacy of touch of a human hand, or the construction of a computer system which can process complex visual signals as well as the human eye and brain are still well beyond the frontiers of modern engineering, but there is little doubt that the engineering problems will be solved sooner or later.

It is however very difficult to conceive of a machine capable of original thought in the human sense. Some eminent AI researchers have suggested that the phenomenon of original thought, at least in the sense we understand it, may only be relevant to us as human beings within our own frame of reference, and that even if true intelligence, original thought, of this kind were possible within a computer system, the conversations which computers might initiate between themselves might be both meaningless and uninteresting to us. It seems therefore unlikely that the popular science fiction vision of the all powerful computer ruling the world will ever actually be fulfilled.

Expert systems – an overview

Perhaps the most widely acclaimed off-shoot from artificial Intelligence research has been the development of a range of computer software, based on specialist knowledge, which attempt to reach some conclusion, to solve some problem, by means similar to those employed by a human expert. Such systems have become known as 'expert systems'.

The concept of expert systems has evolved in response to the need, partially articulated by researchers engaged in the development of improved management information and decision support systems, to develop computer systems which can interact with users in a conversational way, and which can not only recall information from a database but can also develop and pursue a logical line of reasoning. Such systems ought to be able to deduce information from combinations of knowledge already stored in the database and replies given by a user in order to reach conclusions which may not be readily apparent from the raw data originally stored in the system.

The first computer program to be explicitly recognised as an expert system was probably DENDRAL, a system developed at Stanford Research Institute from about 1965 onwards for the inference of chemical structures from mass spectrometer readings. Much research has been carried out since, and Bramer (1982) contains a useful review of the first fifteen years.

The current intense interest in the subject originally stems from the so-called Japanese Fifth Generation Project so widely publicised by people such as d'Agapeyeff (1983) and Feigenbaum and McCorduck (1985).

In the United Kingdom the study of artificial intelligence has had a chequered existence. Whilst research has been on-going in one form or another since the end of the second world war, development in the United Kingdom was virtually strangled by the Lighthill Report, Lighthill (1973), which argued that although systems could be constructed which work in a laboratory, the chances of such systems working satisfactorily in real life situations was small. It was not until the early 1980s that Britain again began to take an official interest in a subject which was already hot news in both America and Japan. The Alvey programme was launched in 1983 in a desperate attempt to catch up with others in the field.

A good 'potted history' of artificial intelligence research is given in Durham (1984), and a more detailed review of earlier work in Michie (1982).

Definition of·an expert system

Before attempting to explore the possible uses of expert systems in quantity surveying and construction, it is first necessary to attempt to define in more precise terms what an expert system is. As with any developing field there have been many attempts to provide formal definitions, ranging from the complex:

> An expert system is a means of capturing the knowledge of experts in the form of programs and data where disagreement among the experts are settled by mediation and the results refined so as to extract the essence of their knowledge in such a way that it can be used by less experienced people within the field...The expert system is a tool and a means of coherent communication of the latest views of the experts to the users who may well be the experts themselves.
>
> (Addis (1981))

to the rather more simple:

> [Expert systems are] ... problem solving programs that solve substantial problems generally conceded as being difficult and requiring expertise. They are called 'knowledge based' because their performance depends critically upon the use of facts and heuristics used by experts.
>
> (Stefik (1982))

Perhaps the most definitive definition is that approved by the British Computer Society Committee of the Specialist Group on Expert Systems reported in d'Agapeyeff (1983):

> An expert system is regarded as the embodiment within the computer of the knowledge based component from an expert skill in such a way that the system can offer intelligent advice or take an intelligent decision about a processing function. A desirable additional characteristic which many would consider fundamental is the ability to justify its own line or reasoning in a manner directly intelligible to the enquirer. The style adopted to attain these characteristics is rule based programming.

although Naylor (1983) sees things in much more simple terms:

> To take an everyday example, there were once people who were payroll experts. In fact some of the most agile minds in the British Empire could have been found in the Army Pay Corps. Adept at finding loopholes, special cases, hitherto unknown allowances, these human experts (some would say 'superhuman') held sway for years. It was simply the payroll

program which sent pay clerks the way of the dinosaur. The payroll program can easily be seen as an example of an expert system – it embodies the total sum of human expertise on the subject of payrolls. But nobody thinks of it like that anymore.

Since we cannot find a comprehensive definition of an expert system, perhaps it would be best to attempt to establish what the characteristics of such a system ought to be. The following is a shortened and paraphrased version of the characteristics identified by Lansdowne (1982), although he is careful to point out that not all systems display all of these properties:

(i)   They know a great deal about a limited but useful area of interest. The knowledge may be aquired from experience but, more likely, from a human expert.

(ii)   They give their advice conversationally in the manner of a human consultant and can understand and respond to simple questions posed in plain, although somewhat specialised, language.

(iii)   Their knowledge is embodied in the form of sets of rules with corresponding actions. This feature makes for easier correction of deficiencies or errors in the knowledge base as well as the acquisition of new knowledge. The knowledge usually exists independently of the program and this should make it possible to use the same program with a variety of knowledge bases able to deal with different tasks.

(iv)   Expert systems often give their advice in probabilistic rather than absolute terms.

(v)   The questions posed by expert systems are limited to those which are relevant to a particular line of reasoning. Thus if at any time the system decides that it has sufficient information to arrive at a conclusion it does not continue to ask questions.

(vi)   Expert systems can explain and justify their reasoning in such a way that experts can accept their credibility and non-experts can learn from them.

Generally research seems to indicate that expert systems may be of most uses where:

(i)   The performance of the task is more dependent upon factual knowledge rather than computational method.

(ii)   The area of interest is limited and specialised.

(iii)   The knowledge base can be built up gradually over a period of time.

(iv)   Consultants exist and are available for consultation.

Types of problem

It has already been shown that management tasks may be sub-divided into a number of overlapping groups depending upon the degree of human intuitition needed to resolve them, and that much work has been carried out in the construction of computer based decision support systems aimed at helping the manager make the most appropriate decision in each case. It has also been shown that the more highly structured a task becomes the more likely it is that a complete computerised solution will be possible.

The types of problem for which computers may provide some assistance may be classified as:

Problems of classification

In this type of problem something needs to be identified or classified upon the basis of observable characteristics, possibly without 100 per cent certainty. This classification will include problems such as medical diagnosis, for which some of the most successful expert systems have been developed (see for example the MYCIN system described in Shortliffe (1976)). In the construction industry similar problems for which expert systems have been developed include the diagnosis of faults in air-conditioning systems (Lansdowne (1982)) and the diagnosis of the causes of damp in buildings by the Building Research Station.

Problems of selection

In this case the problem is to select components from a wide standard range to fit a given set of circumstances. In effect this type of problem is the opposite of the classification problem described above. One well known example is the XCON system developed to configure DEC VAX computer systems, and it is not difficult to see that similar systems could be used for the selection of standard components in prefabricated construction systems.

Problems of data retrieval and interpretation

Many situations are governed by well defined but often extremely complex rules, and the solution to problems can often become clear once the rules are understood. Perhaps the most obvious, and the most complex, manifestation of this type of problem is the Law, where considerable volumes of statute and case law form a large body of rules which guide practitioners in the resolution of disputes. Oakley (1987) gives an introduction to the use of expert systems in law, and a more detailed account is given in Susskind (1987). Oakley (1987) also reports on an expert system developed by

Susskind and Capper called the Latent Damages Advisor which attempts to unravel the mysteries of the Latent Damages Act 1986. Other similar obvious contenders in construction include the various Standard Methods of Measurement, Building Regulations, and the various Planning Acts. Such systems would differ from simple data retrieval systems by being able to respond to queries such as 'List the measurement rules in SMM7 relating to the measurement of concrete formwork' or 'Display the criteria to be satified for a contractor to succeed in an application for payment of loss and expense under the JCT80 form of contract'.

Problems of prediction

Given a set of present circumstances and a knowledge base of past events predict the likelihood of a given event occurring. Naylor (1983) for example includes a simple weather forecasting system which attempts to predict the likelihood of rain tomorrow based on historical data. Mathematical predictive techniques are well known (see for example Green (1980)), and it is easy to see how systems could be constructed to attempt, for example, to predict the future cost of buildings.

Structure of an expert system

Figure 8.1 shows a very simplified representation of what actually happens in real life when a human expert is confronted by a problem. In simple terms the problem is cross-matched with data held in some knowledge base and the result of the merger then governs the advice which is given. Although the above models fairly accurately the way in which a problem is considered in human terms it is not a good model from which to build a comparable computer system.

In practice of course the expert is always expanding his or her knowledge base by reading technical journals, discussions with colleagues etc. This updating of the knowledge base is likely to take place in very technical language which would be largely meaningless to a non-expert. On the other hand however communication between the human expert and the human enquirer is likely to use much less technical language. The computer system therefore needs to make some provision for both modes of communication. In addition human language of any kind is extremely rich and wide-ranging; similar ideas may be expressed in many different ways and the computer system must therefore somehow select the important parts of the problem from the input dialogue. A better representation therefore of an expert system, adapted from Feigenbaum and McCorduck (1985), is given in figure 8.2.

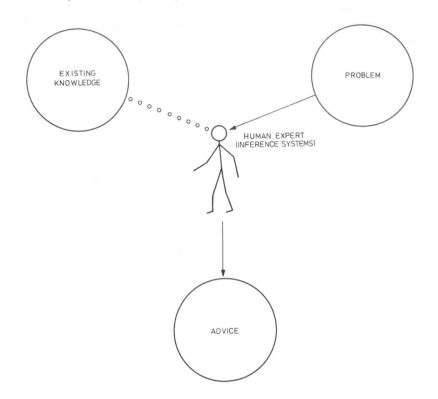

Figure 8.1 The human expert

Elements of an expert system

The knowledge base

The knowledge base is the central reservoir from which the system will ultimately formulate its advice and opinions. The contents of the knowledge base therefore need to comprise far more than mere facts or information. According to Feigenbaum and McCorduck (1985:p. 7), knowledge is '... information which has been pared, shaped, interpreted, selected and trans- formed', and in order to achieve this the knowledge base needs to contain not only the facts about the relevant 'domain' or sphere of activity, but also a representation of the 'weighting' which the human expert would give to those facts; the experience which enables him to provide a balanced judgement or reach a reasoned conclusion about the facts of any particular case. In short the knowledge base must firstly contain a set of 'rules' embodying the facts of the domain, secondly a set of 'goals' denoting possible results and thirdly some mechanism to relate the 'rules' to the 'goals'. The simplest form is obviously shown by the

IF(rule) THEN(goal)

construct indicating that a certain outcome will occur if a certain rule is satisfied. It is sometimes extended to

IF(rule) THEN(goal probability x)

indicating that some uncertainty exists. A number of different mechanisms have been developed and are simply explained in Landowne (1982).

The inference system

The inference mechanism forms the part of the expert system which connects the problem with the information stored in the knowledge base. A number of different mechanisms have been developed, but perhaps the

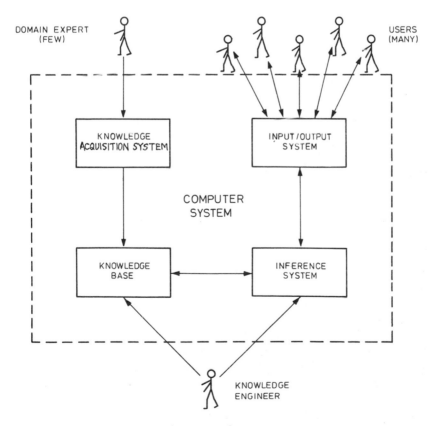

Figure 8.2 Elements of an expert system

two main methods are known as 'forward chaining' and 'backward chaining'.

Forward chaining systems are very effective where the process consists essentially of explaining a complex body of data, for example a system to interpret contract clauses, methods of measurement etc. The inference system is then able to ask questions and establish to what extent the problem data conforms to the rules as declared. In other words, by steadily building upon the information already established the computer is able to move forward through the information base until a conclusion is reached. Forward chaining systems therefore attempt to establish the left-hand side of the

IF(rule) THEN(goal)

statement. Backward chaining systems on the other hand attempt to discover whether a specific situation ('goal') exists, and to therefore fire a rule which would produce that result. They therefore attempt to establish whether the right hand side of the

IF(rule) THEN(goal)

statement is true. Such systems are often described as 'goal driven', and are very useful where the observable information comprises the resultant of some action. Systems attempting to resolve problems of diagnosis often work by backward chaining.

NCC (1987) contains both written examples and computer software illustrating several different types of inference mechanism.

The user input/output system

Expert systems are supposed to be friendly, to help people solve problems. In order to do this effectively people must be able to communicate easily with them, and the system must be able to explain the reasoning behind its conclusions or advice. For many specialists in the field this has meant the use of natural language, and considerable research has been undertaken in this area.

Basically the problem underlying the machine understanding of natural language is quite simple. People using everyday speech employ an enormously wide range of different ways of saying the same thing, of asking the same question, and the construction of computer programs capable of parsing language correctly is extremely difficult. Lansdowne (1982) summarises the main problems very well. In order to overcome these problems many expert systems resort to the use of questions posed by the machine, to which the user is required to make only simple, usually one word, answers.

Most expert systems rely upon the use of a normal keyboard, although other methods of input are possible. Lansdowne (1982) for example proposes the use of an electronic tablet rather like a digitiser menu, and one could easily foresee the use of speech recognition devices in the future.

The knowledge acquisition system

Most experts now agree that the initial knowledge acquisition is best accomplished by a 'knowledge engineer'. Knowledge engineering is a very new skill which is still not completely defined, but the task of the knowledge engineer is to extract the necessary relevant knowledge from the experts and build up the knowledge base of the system.

In general terms the task can be sub-divided into:

(i) A background study. The knowledge engineer needs to study the background material on the subject and become familiar with the jargon in order both that he understands what the expert says, and also in order that the expert's time is not wasted by needless explanation.

(ii) The knowledge engineer must discuss the problem domain with the expert in order to understand the domain boundaries.

(iii) The knowledge engineer must select a problem solving strategy suitable for the particular domain under consideration.

(iv) The knowledge engineer then 'extracts' the appropriate knowledge from the experts and develops an early 'test' version of the system.

(v) Ask the expert to 'use' the draft system and determine whether the output is satisfactory. Ask other experts to use the system and collect a range of opinion.

(vi) Refine the system by repeating steps (iv) and (v) until the experts agree that the result is satisfactory.

Feigenbaum and McCorduck (1985:p. 83) report the development of the following 'rules' for knowledge engineering:

(i) It is very difficult for domain experts to be their own knowledge engineers; an outsider is required in order to see the problem clearly.

(ii) The knowledge engineer must be prepared to throw things away; the first draft will never be acceptable.

(iii) Problems must be carefully chosen and clearly bounded with a need for *specialist* knowledge.

(iv) Knowledge engineers must be flexible, and good communicators on many levels.

(v) If no tools exist to do what is required then build new ones.

(vi) The knowledge engineer needs to develop weighting procedures to cope with statements such as 'I strongly believe...'.

(vii)   The knowledge base must be readily modified.
(viii) The expert system must explain its own reasoning.

Expert system shells

Although the early expert systems such as MYCIN were special purpose tools developed to fulfil specific tasks, it quickly became apparent that the same problem solving process could be used for many different problem domains; that it was possible for the 'inference system' to be, to a large extent, independent of both the actual problem data and the domain knowledge base. Development was therefore concentrated on the construction of 'empty' expert system shells which could, once the domain knowledge base had been added, be used as general purpose problem solvers.

A large number of such shells have been developed in recent years employing a range of different problem solving strategies. As explained earlier some strategies are better at solving some problems than others, and Allwood, Stewart, Hinde & Negus (1985) contains an evaluation of the suitability of various shells for use in the construction industry. NCC (1987) contains examples of a number of different types of system shell.

Expert systems in quantity surveying and construction

In addition to the work cited above, Wager (1984) and Wager (1985) contain good reviews of the use of expert systems in the construction industry as a whole, and both Hamilton (1985) and Shaw (1985) discuss the use of expert systems in building services. It is however in quantity surveying that perhaps the most significant strides have been made to date.

In 1983 the government launched a five-year programme of research under the chairmanship of John Alvey into the possibilities for the use of fifth generation computer systems in British industry. Research initiatives were invited from industry under the provisions of the Alvey programme, and the only successful construction industry submission was made by the RICS for research into the use of expert systems in quantity surveying. Brown (1987) and Davis (1988) describe the research, which was based at Salford University under the supervision of Professor Peter Brandon guided by a group of selected practitioners.

The intention of the project was to investigate the use of expert systems in the stategic planning of construction projects. It was decided to consider four major aspects of the problem viz:

(i)   Financial budgeting and initial cost estimating
(ii)   Choice of procurement method
(iii)   Forecast of construction time
(iv)   Development cost appraisal and profitability

The resultant programme called Elsie (from LC – Lead Consultant), was finally unveiled in the Spring of 1988 for use by members of the Quantity Surveying Division of the RICS. A draft summary report, Brandon (1987b), was published at the end of 1987, and the final report by Brandon, Basden, Hamilton and Stockley (1988) in mid 1988.

The basic operation of Elsie is described in Ashworth (1988 a and b).

Also of interest to those contemplating building expert systems is the practical experience described in Hamilton (1987) and Stockley (1987).

The effect which the widespread use of expert systems will have upon the professions has been the subject of much comment and discussion. Evans (1979) for example wrote at length about the profession's probable decline of influence as the use of computer based information systems becomes more widespread. It is also interesting, in the light of the RICS/Alvey project, to recall that, in 1984, Brandon wrote:

> On the face of it, the professions as a whole seem vulnerable. Their strength lies in being a repository for a unique brand of knowledge. If this knowledge is enshrined within a computer program it becomes available, in time, to a much wider audience.
>
> (Brandon (1984))

One might reflect therefore upon whether the RICS/Alvey project will prove to be truly a success from the point of view of the ordinary quantity surveying practitioner. Brandon however does offer some hope of a lifeline, albeit a treacherous one, when he goes on to write:

However some comfort can be derived from the following:

(i)   Clients will want someone to take the risk for a decision that is being made. The professional practitioner will be expected to take that responsibilty until such time as the risk is negligible or until the computer can be sued!
(ii)   Someone will need to remain the 'domain expert' for updating the system, although in the very long term it may be possible for self learning systems to be developed for certain tasks.
(iii)   Not all the work of a profession can be enshrined in a machine nor will it be desirable to do so. Those aspects involving personal trust and confidence as well as certain creative aspects of judgement will be difficult to replace. Nevertheless it will probably require considerably fewer personnel to provide the professional service.

(Brandon (1984))

In the final analysis quantity surveyors and other professionals must accept and embrace the spread of 'smart' computer systems; to consider doing otherwise would be as foolish as Canute attempting to halt the tide. If the quantity surveying profession is to thrive however it must also evolve, must transcend those highly structured rule based tasks for which the computer provides an acceptable alternative in favour of those much less structured tasks involving the exercise of human judgement. In the past a high premium has been placed on those quantity surveyors who knew intimately all of the rules of measurement, and could recite forms of contract, but these are the very people who, in the future, face the prospect of being upstaged in the same way as Naylor's payroll experts. Perhaps in the future, although a working knowledge of the relevant rules will still be essential, much greater emphasis will be placed on the inter-personal skills of, for example, management, communication and negotiation.

'Intelligent' management information and decision support systems

This chapter began with a discussion on management information and decision support systems, and attempted to show how this branch of computer science influenced some early expert systems; the MYCIN medical diagnosis program for example, described in Shortliffe (1976), is generally accepted as being an expert system, but since it expresses its results in probabilistic terms leaving the final decision on interpretation to the consultant, it may also be seen as a decision support system.

It is perhaps therefore fitting to conclude with the idea that expert systems may now be combined with management information to provide managers with 'intelligent' decision support systems which will assist with those less structured tasks involving large volumes of information to which expert systems alone are not well suited.

Research into this process of combining artificial intelligence and conventional databases is still very new; in fact as recently as 1984 Thomas (1984), whilst discussing the theory of such systems, wrote:

> There is probably no working example yet of either an intelligent DSS (decision support system) or a Problem Solver.

More recently however Jones (1987) reports the development of a number of such systems both in America and in the United Kingdom and it seems likely that this marriage of artificial intelligence and management information systems will make possible the creation of a new generation of decision support packages to aid the manager in the 1990s.

References

Addis T.R. (1981) 'Definition of an expert system' *British Computer Society Specialist Group on Expert Systems Newsletter no.3* Spring/Summer 1981

Allwood R.S., Stewart D.S., Hinde C.and Negus B. (1985) *Evaluations of expert systems shells for construction industry applications* Loughborough University of Technology

Anthony R.N. (1965) *Planning and control systems – a framework for analysis* Harvard University Graduate School of Business Administration

Ashworth G. (1988a) 'Elsie Plans Her Budget' *Building* 24/6/88 pp. 60–61

Ashworth G. (1988b) 'Go ask Elsie' *Building* 1/7/88 pp. 50–51

Bennett J. (1983) (ed.) *Building decision support systems* Addison-Wesley

Bramer M.A. (1982) 'A survey and critical review of expert systems research' in *Introductory readings in expert systems* D.Michie (ed.) Gordon & Breach

Brandon P.S. (1984) *Computers: friend or foe?* Department of Surveying, Portsmouth Polytechnic

Brandon P.S. (1987a) *Building Cost Modelling and Computers* E. & F.N. Spon

Brandon P.S. (1987b) *Draft summary final report, Alvey community club project, the application of expert systems to quantity surveying* Royal Institution of Chartered Surveyors

Brandon P.S., Basden A, Hamilton I., and Stockley J. (1988) *Expert systems: the strategic planning of construction projects* Royal Institution of Chartered Surveyors

Brown G. (1987) 'RICS/Alvey expert systems research' *Chartered Quantity Surveyor* April 1987 pp. 15–16

d'Agapeyeff A. (1983) *Expert systems, Fifth Generation and UK suppliers* National Computing Centre

Davis L. (1988) 'Inside Information' *Chartered Quantity Surveyor* January 1988 pp. 17–19

Dearden J. (1966) 'Myth of real time management information' *Harvard Buisiness Review* Vol.44 No.3 pp. 123–132

Durham A. (1984) 'Fifth generation fever' *Practical Computing* October 1984 pp. 115–117

Evans C. (1979) *The mighty micro* Coronet Books

Feigenbaum E. and McCorduck P. (1985)*The fifth generation* Addison-Wesley

Gorry G.A. and Krumland R.B. (1983) 'Artificial intelligence research and decision support systems' in *Building decision support systems* Bennett J. (ed.) Addison Wesley

Green A. (1980) 'Future perfect?' *Personal Computer World* November 1980

Hamilton G. (1985) *Expert systems in building services* Paper presented at the 1985 Construction Industry Computing Association Construction Expert Conference

Hamilton I. (1987) 'Developing expert systems for management applications' in *Building Cost Modelling and Computers* Brandon P. (ed.) E. & F.N. Spon

Jones R. (1987) 'Expert support systems' *Computer Weekly* 26/3/87

Kanter J. (1977) *Management orientated management information systems* Prentice Hall

Keen P.G.W. and Scott-Morton M.S. (1978) *Decision support systems – an organizational perspective* Addison-Wesley

Lansdowne J. (1982) *Expert systems: Their impact on the construction industry* RIBA Conference Fund

Lighthill J. (1973) *Report on artificial intelligence – Report of a committee chaired by Sir James Lighthill* Science Research Council

Michie D. (1982) (ed.) *Introductory readings in expert systems* Gordon & Breach

Moore J.H. and Chang M.G. (1983) 'Meta design considerations in building decision support systems' in *Building decision support systems* Bennett J. (ed.) Addison Wesley

Naylor C. (1983) *Build your own expert system* Sigma Technical Press

NCC (1987) *Expert systems starter pack* National Computing Centre

Nolan R.L. and Gibson C.F. (1974) 'Managing the four stages of EDP growth' *Harvard Business Review* Vol.52 No.1 pp. 76–78

Oakley K. (1987) 'Legal eagles' *Expert Systems User* November 1987

Shaw M.R. (1985) *Expert systems – an objective view* Paper presented at the 1985 Conference on Computers in Building and Services Design, Nottingham University

Shortliffe E.H. (1976) *MYCIN: Computer based medical consultations* Elsevier North Holland

Simon H.A. (1960) *The new science of management decision making* Harper & Row

Stefik M. (1982) et al. 'The organisation of expert systems – a tutorial' *Artificial Intelligence* Vol.18 No.2

Stockley J.E. (1987) 'Knowledge acquisition for expert systems' in *Building Cost Modelling and Computers* Brandon P. (ed.) E. & F.N. Spon

Suskind R. (1987) *Expert systems in law* Oxford University Press

Thomas R. (1984) 'Knowledge base techniques for decision support for management' *BCS Specialist Group on Expert Systems Newsletter No.11* June 1984 pp. 13–15

Wager D.M. (1984) *Expert systems and the construction industry* Construction Industry Computing Association

Wager D.M. (1985) *The future of expert systems in construction management* Construction Industry Computing Association

Computers Applied to
Quantity Surveying

9 Computers in Cost Planning

Objectives

At the end of this chapter you will be able to:

- Discuss the use of computers for the collection of cost data and the preparation of budget estimates.
- Comment on the use of computerised estimating systems by the quantity surveyor.
- Comment on the use of on-line cost information systems.
- Comment on the use of computers in predicting cost trends.
- Discuss the use of computers in cost modelling

Computers in quantity surveying

Whereas the early part of this book examined a number of issues associated with the use of computers in an office environment, this second section now considers the use of computers, in particular quantity surveying activities. It is however most important to recognise that although, for convenience, I have chosen to sub-divide this part into separate chapters dealing with cost planning, the production of bills of quantities, post contract work, project management and computer aided design, in reality each of these areas overlaps with all of the others and it is totally artificial to consider any one area in isolation. Thus, for example, although a facility for cost analysis of tender bills is often provided by the vendors of bill production systems the collection of the data is essentially, by definition, a post tender process, although the information collected is actually used during the initial cost advice stage. Close associations also exist between cost planning, bill production and computer aided design; and project management in a way embraces the whole spectrum of activities. It is therefore most important to recognise the links which exist and to appreciate that each of the separate topics is in fact merely a part of a coherent whole.

Cost planning and cost modelling

Cost planning as a formal process in the United Kingdom began to emerge during the years immediately following the Second World War, largely because of an increasing amount of construction activity in the central and local government funded sectors. Local authorities of the time faced not only strict centrally imposed cash limits upon annual expenditure, but also centrally imposed government expenditure ceilings upon the cost of all new building. Such restrictions required that local authorities should be able to predict tender values for specific building projects in order to make sure that the tender eventually obtained would be within the approved cash limit, and quantity surveyors therefore needed to develop means of costing the architect's design.

Initially then the process was little more than an estimating function involving costing the completed design; the easiest method was simply to measure the quantities of work involved and price them in accordance with rates derived from previously tendered schemes which had themselves proved to be within the required cost guidelines. The process was therefore essentially linear in that the design was completed to some pre-defined stage, the cost was checked and if found to be excessive the design was revised.

During the 1960s, however, the search for innovative building forms within the constraints of rigidly enforced cash limits required these cost estimating techniques to be refined and adapted in order that the cost of the design could be assessed as the process progressed; thus quantity surveyors developed elemental cost checking techniques whereby the total budget available for a project was broken down into a number of functional elements such as foundations, external walls, internal walls etc., the cost of each of which could be checked individually as required throughout the design process. Cost thus began, in theory at least, to have some effect upon the development of the design, in that if an architect wished to overspend the budget on one part of the scheme other compensating savings must be made elsewhere or the client must agree to revise the budget. It was therefore considered that the distribution of cost throughout the design could be planned. Quantity surveyors still however relied heavily upon measurement of the work and the use of cost data derived from previously let schemes as their major cost control tools, and in fact Morrison and Stevens (1980) report that their 1979 survey of current cost planning practice revealed that these techniques of measurement and valuation were still the most commonly used. A fuller account of contemporary cost planning practice is given in PSA (1981).

During the late 1970s and early 1980s a number of practitioners began to realise that these traditional methods of cost planning left much to be desired. Smith (1980) summed up the problem when he wrote:

One weakness of cost planning as traditionally practiced is that it starts too late in the design process to have maximum influence. Often it is little more than an estimating service, costing design decisions being already taken.

In addition clients had become aware that the tender price of a project in many cases no longer represented the most significant proportion of the project cost. Huge rises in the cost of energy during the 1970s caused building owners and developers to consider not only the capital cost of the building but also the on-going revenue cost, and such factors of course began to have a profound effect not only upon the design of individual elements but more so upon the initial conception of building form. It was plainly apparent that cost planning had to begin even before sketch plans were prepared if the client was to achieve maximum value for money, and furthermore some mechanism had to be developed to allow a number of alternative design concepts to be evaluated and compared, not only in terms of capital cost but in terms of total cost profile. A cost model was required which would permit 'what-if' simulations in order to establish the 'best fit' solution for each individual client and each individual project. Maver (1979) describes a number of such 'cost models' developed in the Abacus unit at the University of Strathclyde, and Smith (1980) describes the use of such techniques in local authority school building.

Despite early enthusiasm in some quarters, however, modelling techniques such as these have not achieved general acceptance within the profession as a whole. Brandon and Newton (1986) comment that:

> For twenty years huge amounts of time and money have gone into the development of models to improve building cost forecasting and management. But an investigation of quantity surveying offices would reveal an almost exclusive concentration on approximate quantities in various stages of refinement, often used too late in the design process to be effective in influencing the design.

Despite this lack of acceptance some commentators such as Beeston (1983) and Newton (1986) contend that the quantity surveyor should make more use of even more sophisticated mathematical and statistical tools in the modelling process.

Computers and cost planning

Cost planning is not an exact science, and most quantity surveyors specialising in cost planning would regard a subjective 'feeling' for the project to be a valuable tool in their professional tool kit. No two projects are exactly the same, and the cost planner must somehow take account not only of the building and its site, the peculiarities of the architect etc., but also must consider and make some allowance for factors such as market conditions. Even more difficult to foresee are factors such as the work-load of tendering contractors and their keenness or otherwise to win the contract; factors which the cost planner has no way of evaluating with any degree of accuracy. There is therefore it seems little chance of a completely automated cost planning system, but computers can nonetheless have a valuable role to play in cost planning, in the collection and analysis of historical cost data, in the processing of cost estimates and in the dynamic evaluation of alternative design solutions through the medium of cost models.

It should however also be pointed out that modern cost planning is essentially an iterative and interactive process, and that whilst some attempts were made to use mainframe computer systems it is only really during the last ten years that computers have become widely used in this field.

Cost analysis

We have already seen that many of the quantity surveyor's traditional cost planning processes depend upon the collection and analysis of historical cost data gathered from accepted tenders, and facilities to carry out cost analysis of this kind have long been provided as an 'add-on' to Bill production packages. The scope of such programs tends to vary somewhat from system to system, but the level of analysis available depends of course upon the level to which the original information has been coded (see also the discussion in chapter 10 entitled 'Data labelling').

The extent of data labelling required to analyse a project into, for example, the form required by the RICS Standard Form of Cost Analysis, may be very time consuming and may prove not to be cost effective unless the labelled data is to be used for some other purpose, for example to resort a work section tender Bill into elemental form for contract management purposes. In addition, although most cost analysis data is presented in the form of elemental cost/square metre of floor area, what is often required for future cost estimates is the cost/unit area of a given element, for example the cost/m² of external wall where the cost is related to the area of external wall rather than to the floor area of the building. This cost is usually called the 'element unit rate' (EUR), and some programs have provided facilities for this to be calculated. They do however in general require the input of the quantity of each element, the 'element unit quantity' (EUQ), and the calculation of element unit rates is often done more quickly without using the computer at all.

Tender price indexing

One of the major problems encountered in using historical cost data for the planning of new projects concerns the difficulty of adjusting tender price data to take account of time. A study carried out in 1970 at the University of London developed a method of indexing tenders using a comparison of the 'price important' items in a given scheme with a standard price schedule. The methodology developed is described in Mitchell (1971), and the method is now in common use and forms a major feature of the RICS Building Cost Information Service (BCIS).

The method, although not difficult to apply manually, requires a good deal of calculation and a number of practitioners have developed small computer programs of their own to handle the arithmetic involved.

Others have gone further and have used a file of tender price indices as input to other computer programs employing statistical techniques to predict future cost trends. Whilst services such as the BCIS do calculate and publish predicted cost trends, the values calculated are often on a national basis, and the national trend can sometimes be widely different from that shown in a particular region. Some practitioners with sizeable building programs in a small geographical area, for example local authorities, have found it useful to develop programs of this type for their own use, and experience seems to show that fairly reliable forecasts can be made up to twelve or fifteen months ahead using these techniques.

Cost estimating

The use of computers for cost estimating involves using the machine to interface with some kind of database of cost information. Cost information databases have been constructed using both historical cost analysis data derived from previously tendered projects, and also using rates built up from basic principles using current prices for labour, materials and plant. Both methods have their supporters; the users of basic price data point out that use of historical cost analyses is fraught with pitfalls since the method and accuracy of pricing of previous schemes is unknown, whilst the supporters of the historical approach contend that use of basic price data takes no account of the competitiveness of tenderers or the state of the market, and is in any event difficult unless some design decisions have already been taken. Nonetheless both methods continue to be used.

As regards computer systems based on historical data, the majority work by allowing the user to select from the database one or more cost analyses from previous schemes which are as much like the present project as possible in size, function etc. The analyses selected are then adjusted to take account of time and location to bring them all to a common base, and are then aggregated in some way to form a cost plan for the new scheme. The BCIS 'On-line' service (see below) offers facilities of this type.

Those practitioners preferring to work from basic price data have a number of systems available to them. Systems of this type generally incorporate files of basic materials prices, labour constants, plant costs and outputs in much the same way as those included in a builder's price book; in fact some use systems originally developed to aid contractors in the preparation of tenders. Such systems tend to be used mainly for cost estimating once sketch designs have been produced, and the input options available often include direct entry of dimensions with the computer then performing an elementary abstracting and billing process. Some systems include rudimentary libraries of descriptions similar to but less compre-hensive than those included in packages for the production of Bills of Quantities. Some systems make provision for digitised input. A more complex system of this type is described in Holes (1987).

Many computer aided design systems include cost estimating routines, most of which work by building up prices from basic rate information stored with the graphical components, and the integration of computer aided design and the provision of early cost advice is discussed further in chapter 12.

The BCIS On-line service

The RICS Building Cost Information Service has provided a centralised information exchange for quantity surveyors' cost data since the early 1960s, and in the early 1980s began to establish a computer based cost data bank which could be accessed directly by subscribers through their own office computer systems via the public telephone system. At the same time an approximate estimating package was introduced as an integral part of the service in order that subscribers could manipulate the data extracted from the database on their own office computers, and thus produce cost plans for new schemes. A more detailed description of the system is given in Pegg (1987).

The system appears to function adequately from a technical point of view, although some users have found the speed of data transfer rather slow. The system offers considerable potential although it appears that at present comparatively few quantity surveyors use the service on a regular basis.

Cost modelling

The majority of innovative work associated with the use of computers in this field has, in recent years, been concentrated on the development of cost modelling systems in which the quantity surveyor is able not only to represent the total cost profile of a project but also to interact with the model; to indulge in 'what-if' simulations as the design progresses in order to attempt to ensure the best possible fit between the clients' requirements and the completed scheme. The most complete current account of work in this field is probably Brandon (1987).

A number of approaches to cost modelling have been explored, and the rapid development of powerful low cost computer systems capable of handling large volumes of data has intensified the effort in recent years.

The majority of existing cost models have employed familiar historical cost data gathered from cost analyses as described above, but have attempted to use the power of the microcomputer to allow the user to interact directly with the data. A nice example of this type of model is that described by Brandon (1985). Whilst many system developers have written purpose built computer programs for the task, Williams (1987) describes an example of this type of model developed using a three-dimensional spreadsheet as the development tool.

Other researchers have advocated other types of model. Brandon and Newton (1986) for example describe the beginnings of an expert system christened GUIDE (Graphical User Interrogation of Development Economics), and this approach has been carried even further through the joint RICS/Alvey research programme project considering the use of expert systems in the strategic planning of construction projects. The results of the research are described in Brandon, Basden, Hamilton and Stockley (1988). Expert system techniques as applied here however simply attempt to use the computer to reproduce the reasoning process used by the human expert in the solution of cost planning problems, and therefore whilst the research conducted by Brandon et al is a breakthrough in its own right such systems may prove of limited use if it can be shown that the human model upon which they are based is itself either defective, inefficient or flawed.

Some workers in the field have proposed that the intuitive methods commonly used at present by cost planners are defective in that they make little attempt to take account of construction management issues; they are essentially concerned with predicting costs on the basis of an average of that which has gone before and they make little allowance for the planning and constructional difficulties of any one particular scheme. It is for this reason that some researchers in the field advocate radically different types of cost model. Beeston (1987) for example proposes the use of three alternative techniques which attempt to model the construction process itself either by the simulation of construction in detail, attaching costs to activity networks or by simulation of construction planning. The development of this type of system is described in Bennett and Ferry (1987) and by Bowen, Wolvaardt and Taylor (1987). Techniques such as these have obvious overlaps with computer software developed for project management, and it may well be that closer integration of the management and cost modelling functions will in due course become inevitable.

Conclusion

It can clearly be seen from the above that the drive to provide the client with ever more accurate and reliable early cost advice is seen by some to be one of the major areas of development in the field of 'traditional' quantity surveying. The development of the necessary techniques is seen by some to require the use of extremely sophisticated mathematical and statistical techniques for which the use of computer systems is seen as essential. On the other hand however the costing tools used most often by the majority of quantity surveyors in their day-to-day work are still shown to be those of approximate measurement and valuation, but even in this case the advice is usually required very quickly if the design process is not to be disrupted. The drive for greater and greater speed in the pre-contract process, together with the use of contractual techniques which allow overlap between the design and construction phases must mean that the use of computers in this field will continue to increase.

Taking the broader view it can be seen that all of the different techniques discussed above are likely to have some part to play in the costing process. At the very beginning of a scheme, when a developer is attempting perhaps to assess the viability of a new building as opposed to a rehabilitation, before any design decisions are taken, there is an obvious use for interactive models, perhaps using more advanced mathematical and statistical methods to manipulate historical data, implemented in the form of expert systems, but as the design progresses there is an equally obvious need for more traditional techniques based on the familiar principles of measurement and valuation. Such techniques must however be implemented in a form which allows design decisions to be evaluated dynamically as the design progresses. For the majority of schemes such techniques will probably be sufficient, but for larger and more complex projects, in particular perhaps those designed using computer aided design systems, models taking account of the construction process will probably be required, and one can I think expect to see closer integration between computer aided design systems, cost models and project management software.

Whatever the eventual outcome it is obvious that the area of pre-contract cost advice is one in which there is considerable scope for the development of new techniques and increasing application of computer systems if the industry is to be able to provide the clients of the future with the building they require at the right price, at the right time and to the right quality.

References

Beeston D. (1983) *Statistical methods for building price data* E. & F.N. Spon

Beeston D. (1987) 'A future for cost modelling' in *Building, cost modelling and computers* Brandon P.S. (ed) E. & F.N. Spon

Bennett J. and Ferry D. (1987) 'Towards a simulated model of the total construction process' in *Building, cost modelling and computers* Brandon P.S. (ed) E. & F.N. Spon

Bowen P.A., Wolvaardt J.S. and Taylor R.G. (1987) 'Cost modelling: a process modelling approach' in *Building, cost modelling and computers* Brandon P.S. (ed).

Brandon P.S. (1985) 'Data on tap' *Chartered Quantity Surveyor* March 1985 pp. 300–302

Brandon P.S. (1987) *Building, cost modelling and computers* E. & F.N. Spon

Brandon P.S. and Newton S. (1986) 'Improving the forecast' *Chartered Quantity Surveyor* May 1986 pp. 24–26

Brandon P.S., Basden A., Hamilton I., and Stockley J. (1988) *Expert systems: the strategic planning of construction projects* Royal Institution of Chartered Surveyors

Holes L.G. (1987) 'Holistic resource and cost modelling' in *Building, cost modelling and computers* Brandon P.S. (ed).

Maver T. (1979) 'Cost performance modelling' *Chartered Quantity Surveyor* December 1979 pp. 111–115

Mitchell R. (1971) 'A tender based building price index' *Chartered Surveyor* July 1971

Morrison N. and Stevens S. (1980) 'Cost planning in theory and in practice: A construction cost database' *Chartered Quantity Surveyor* June 1980 pp. 313–315

Pegg I.D. (1987) 'Computerised approximate estimating from the BCIS On-line database' in *Building, cost modelling and computers* Brandon P.S. (ed).

PSA (1981) *Cost planning and computers* Department of the Environment Property Services Agency

Smith G. (1980) 'Cost planning the design process' *Chartered Quantity Surveyor* August 1980 pp. 13–16

Williams G.R. (1987) 'The development of a spreadsheet application for the cost modelling of buildings during the early design stages' in *Building, cost modelling and computers* Brandon P.S. (ed).

10 Computers and Bills of Quantity

Objectives

At the end of this chapter you will be able to:

- Discuss the factors to be considered when considering the purchase of a bills of quantities system.
- Explain the advantages and disadvantages of standard libraries of description.
- Discriminate between the various types of billing system available and identify their strengths and weaknesses.
- Discuss the advantages and disadvantages of computerised measurement systems.

Computers and Bills of Quantities

It has already been shown (chapter 1) that, collectively, quantity surveyors have, for some 30 years, devoted more time and effort to the development of computer systems for the production of Bills of Quantities than to all of the other applications of the technology put together. The struggle to develop computerised billing systems which are both cost effective and easy to use has over the years assumed something of the fervour of the quest for the Holy Grail; unfortunately cynics, of whom the quantity surveying profession seems to possess a large number, would no doubt say that to date both enterprises have met with approximately equal success in that none of the billing systems presently available has proved sufficiently attractive to persuade a majority of practitioners to subscribe to its use. Nor is it that the rank and file of the profession are averse to change. The rapid spread of cut and shuffle techniques during the early 1960s is ample proof if proof were needed that practitioners are only too willing to change their methods if it can be seen that there are clear advantages in doing so. One is therefore forced to assume that since only a minority of firms use computerised billing techniques there are, despite continuous and no doubt highly expensive advertising campaigns, presently no systems available for purchase which can clearly be shown to be sufficiently cost effective for general use.

Although it is true that there has been no widespread adoption of computerised billing techniques across the profession as a whole, and despite the fact that some commentators continue to predict the imminent demise of the Bill of Quantities as a contract document, there are nonetheless a substantial number of billing systems available on the market, and a substantial number of active users. It is not the intention of this chapter to present any kind of survey or review of the packages available, rather to explore the kinds of facilities commonly offered, to consider the strengths and weaknesses of the various approaches used and to discuss those factors which ought to be considered when contemplating the purchase of a system.

It is also necessary to point out at this point that many of the so-called computer billing packages available for purchase are aimed not at the professional quantity surveyor preparing Bills of Quantities in the accepted sense, but rather at the small builder producing 'builders quantities' for projects let on a 'plan and specification' basis.

Another important distinction which must be recognised is that between those computer systems primarily designed for building works and those designed for use in civil engineering.

Whilst this chapter is primarily concerned with systems for building work, systems for the production of 'builders quantities' and those for use in civil engineering are also briefly described.

Computerised billing systems – a comparison with manual methods

The sequence of operations for the manual production of a Bill of Quantities is shown in figure 10.1, and it has already been shown (chapter 1) that the original spur to development of the first systems came largely from the observation that the 'working-up' stage of the process had begun to become very expensive; to 'absorb an inordinate proportion of fees' (RICS 1961). The working-up process was seen to be largely mechanical in nature, and initial development thus concentrated on the automation of this process. A number of computer systems currently available follow this model, which might be defined as a 'basic' bill production system. The sequence of operations involved in using a system of this type is shown in figure 10.2, and comparison with figure 10.1 will reveal that:

(i)   The abstracting and billing stage, originally requiring considerable skilled labour, has now been mechanised thus reducing the amount of skilled labour required for the process as a whole.

(ii)   In order that the computer can collect 'like' items and

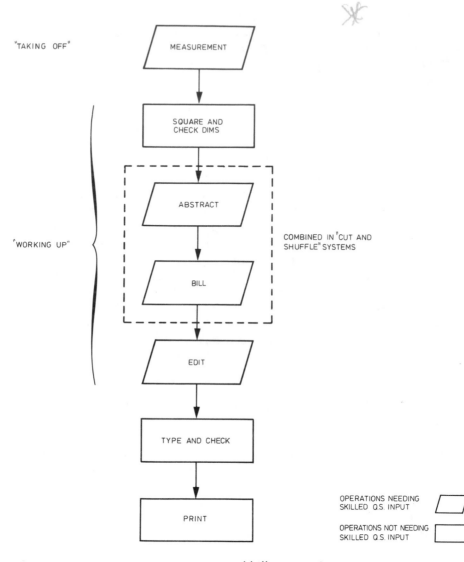

Figure 10.1 Manual bill preparation

subsequently sort them into the correct bill sequence an additional semi-skilled 'coding' process has been introduced. Various coding techniques have been employed from time to time and are considered in more detail below. A further 'data entry' process then follows during which the coded information is entered into the computer.

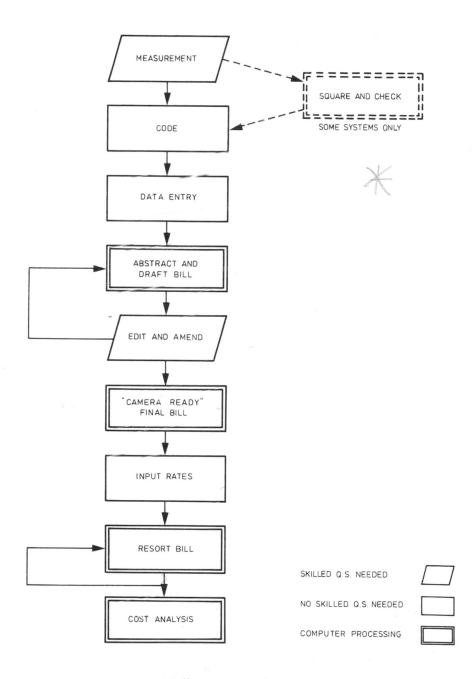

Figure 10.2 Bill preparation by computer (basic system)

(iii) Some systems require the dimensions to be squared before the coded information is entered to the computer, whereas some allow the entry of 'raw' (i.e. un-squared) dimensions with the computer then doing the necessary calculations. Whilst it might, at first sight, appear obvious that dimensions should be squared by the machine, mathematical calculation is after all what the machine is supposed to be good at, some system developers take the view that it is quicker and less prone to error for dimensions to be separately squared and checked by unskilled labour using a pocket calculator.

(iv) A 'feedback loop' has been introduced into the process at the abstracting stage allowing correction, amendment or alteration of the data followed by re-processing of the draft bill as many times as is necessary to ensure absolute correctness before final printing.

(v) The total process has been extended to allow the contractor's tender prices to be added to the information already stored in the machine. Some systems also provide the facility to 're-sort' the information into alternative forms, thus allowing, for example, a bill in SMM work section order for tender purposes and another in priced elemental form for post contract management, valuations and the production of the final account.

(vi) Some systems also provide facilities to allow the automatic production of elemental cost analyses from the priced data.

In view of the above it can clearly be seen that computerised bill production systems provide not only automated production of the bill, but also for subsequent re-use of the data in both the post-contract and the pre-contract fields, and occasionally developers have maximised this facility through the production of other software packages dealing with pre and post contract functions. Perhaps the best known of these totally integrated systems is the Ripac system developed by Rider Hunt and partners reviewed by Hunt (1985).

The whole process only works however at the expense of additional 'coding' and data entry operations, and there is therefore unlikely to be any direct saving in time or cost in the actual preparation of the Bill. The major cost saving will probably accrue from the computer producing a 'camera ready' final print ready for duplication, thus eliminating the costly and time consuming typing stage required with the manual process. One must also however add that the development of 'cut and shuffle' techniques, which occurred in parallel with some of the original computer developments, also enabled quantity surveyors to make considerable savings in working-up costs and the cost advantages of a computer system such as that shown in figure 10.2 over a cut and shuffle system must be regarded as marginal at best.

Much effort has been devoted over the years to improving the cost effectiveness of computerised bill production systems, most commonly by:

(i) simplifying the coding process
(ii) development of electronic measurement tools mainly based on digitisers
(iii) development of 'automated measurement' techniques whereby the computer 'measures' detailed quantities for a particular assembly from 'global' information provided by the taker-off. Perhaps the most common application has been in housing where quantities for standard house types are stored in computer libraries and may be recalled and merged with specific project information by simply quoting the house type reference. Such techniques have been given a variety of names, but are perhaps best known as 'unit quantities'. An example of the use of such a technique is given in Alvey (1976) pp. 99–114.

Each of the above is considered in more detail below.

The coding process

Automation of the abstracting and billing process requires the computer to perform two quite separate and distinct functions:

(i) 'like' items must be collected together and the quantities summed
(ii) the cumulative items generated in (i) above must be sorted into an acceptable 'bill' order.

The human worker-up, either abstracting traditionally or using a cut and shuffle system can manage both of these tasks quite easily; he is able to read and understand the descriptions written by the taker-off and, within limits, is readily able to compensate for the fact that different takers-off may describe the same item in subtly different ways and may not always use precisely the same terminology. He can, in short, use his powers of discrimination to decide when two items should be added together and when they should be kept separate. In addition, because the human worker-up is able to understand the meaning of the written description, he is also able to apply a series of rules enabling him to sort the items into bill order.

This is not the case, however, with the computer. We have already seen that the computer has no innate intelligence; it must be programmed, must be explicitly instructed precisely which items are to be added together and in what order they are to sorted for the final Bill. The application of traditional computing techniques means that items to be added together must be identical in every respect for the process to be successful, and the difficulties involved in using a computer to sort pieces of text of varying length into an acceptable order using the same rules as those employed by the human worker-up were seen as unsurmountable by early system developers. It was therefore considered necessary to convert each item to a code which the computer could then use both to collect like items together and also to sort the cumulative items into a predefined order.

This necessity for a code to be attached to each measured item led directly to the need for some kind of reference manual which the coder could use, in which every description was listed together with its code. This manual came to be known as a 'library of descriptions', and the vast majority of billing systems currently available still use the coded library approach. Indeed there have been those (e.g. Dent 1964) who have predicted that, in time, takers-off would simply write down the code rather than the description thus eliminating the separate coding process. Unfortunately, however, in most systems the code was simply a string of alphanumeric characters which, with very few exceptions were totally devoid of human meaning without reference to the coding manual, and the difficulties inherent in subsequently following taking-off expressed entirely in codes were too great for the idea to achieve any kind of widespread acceptance.

Standard libraries of description

It has already been shown that the use of computers for Bill preparation led directly to the need for a library of standard descriptions, and this was in reality only a small extension of an already common practice in many offices. Most firms of any size had an 'office standard' for descriptions, even if this only consisted of following descriptions used in previous Bills, and the idea of a formal library of descriptions for computer use was not in itself remarkable.

What was perhaps more remarkable was the view taken by the RICS and others, that the use of computers would lead directly to the the use of one standard library of descriptions for use across the entire industry. The RICS working party investigating the use of computers for working up said, in 1961:

> Standardised descriptions are ultimately inevitable. This is in some measure already done in some individual offices and departments but in due course it must come for the profession as a whole.

> Standardisation of descriptions ... would we feel help the industry to build more cheaply. It would do so by assisting work study and thus keen estimating.

> (RICS 1961)

The perceived advantages of industry-wide standard descriptions have historically been listed as:

(i)   Standard descriptions would improve the quality of written communication because the same thing would always be described in the same way.

(ii) This standardisation would make life easier for estimators in pricing and for quantity surveyors attempting to compare historical prices for the same items of work.

(iii) The drafting of descriptions could be simplified, much of the work could be done by junior staff and editing procedures could be largely eliminated and replaced by routine checks.

Many quantity surveyors saw in the above an implied criticism of their much prized skill in accurately describing the work to be carried out. It is not therefore particularly surprising that, despite the backing given to the idea by a number of eminent surveyors and the publication of several standard libraries for manual use, of which the best known is probably that developed by Fletcher and Moore, the universal use of standard descriptions has remained a pipe dream. Many practices, it would appear, whilst using an 'office' standard library for their own convenience still prefer their Bills of Quantities to have a recognisable 'house style'. Others disagree with the way in which discursive English in descriptions has been replaced by staccato descriptions composed of phrases selected from a library and separated by semi-colons. It is argued by some, convincingly in my view, that to blindly take options from a library can actually result in a less accurate description of the work than that which would result from careful and accurate use of discursive English.

Thus it is that in 1988, some 27 years after the RICS working party declared that standard descriptions were inevitable, the use of the Library of Descriptions published for use with SMM7 (HMSO 1988) is still optional. Contrast this with the civil engineering profession where the CESMM2 method of measurement embodies a mandatory library of standard descriptions.

Types of library and coding structure

The simplest type of standard library would be one in which each complete description were allocated a code. This type of library is therefore analogous to the use of a Bill of Quantities from a previous job where the code for a given item might simply be the page and item reference. If such a bill were to be stored in a computer one could therefore 'code' dimensions for a new project by using the page and item reference of the previous Bill, and the computer would therefore be able to use the codes so allocated both to collect like items together and to sort the items in the new project into an acceptable order.

The basic problem with a library of this type is that to offer comprehensive coverage of all items, sizes and specifications likely to be encountered it would need to be very large indeed. In order to be workable therefore the library must be reduced to a skeleton form, with 'blanks' inserted for all size also some specification information. This 'missing' information is then included with items for the new project as a part of the code, and the computer substitutes the actual information provided for the 'blanks' in the library. This type of library has been used in a number of systems; Cyril Sweet & Partners claimed, in 1978, to have developed a comprehensive library of this type running to only 200 pages. (Sweet 1978).

More common is the 'articulated phrase' library in which descriptions are de-composed into smaller constituent phrases each of which is then given a code. Perhaps the most common method of de-composition is to break descriptions down into a number of functional parts. Such an approach requires descriptions to be phrased in a structured form, for example the unstructured description:

One brick wall in Class B engineering bricks (BS 3921) in cement mortar (1:3)

could be expressed in a rather more structured form, and using SMM7 terminology as:

Masonry...........................Primary SMM7 division

Brick/block walling................SMM7 sub-division

Engineering bricks BS 3921
Class B in cement mortar (1:3).....Specification

Walls..............................Description of work

One brick thick....................Size information

Once descriptions are organised in this structured form each component can be considered separately, and lists may be constructed for each in such a way that 'whole' descriptions may be constructed by taking one selection from each list. The structural components of the whole description are often known as 'levels' or 'facets', and part of a simple SMM7 library constructed on this model might look like this:

Primary SMM7 division

Code Description

.

.

C Demolition/Alteration/Renovation
D Groundwork
E Insitu concrete/Large precast concrete
F Masonry
G Structural/Carcassing metal/timber

.

.

SMM7 sub-division

Code Description
F10 Brick/block walling
F11 Glass block walling
F20 Natural stone rubble walling
...
...

Specification

Code Description
...
...
F10 Common bricks BS 3921 in cement mortar (1:3)
F20 Engineering bricks BS 3921 Class B in cement mortar (1:3)
F30 Engineering bricks BS 3921 Class A in cement mortar (1:3)
...
...

Description of work

Code Description

F10 Walls
F20 Isolated piers
F30 Isolated casings
F40 Chimney stacks
...
...

Size information

Code Description

F10 Half brick thick
F20 One brick thick
F30 One and a half bricks thick
...
...

The code for the item in question can therefore be formed by taking the code for each facet and combining them together thus:

F   Masonry

F10   Brick/Block walling

F20   Engineering bricks BS 3921 Class B in cement mortar (1:3)

F10   Walls

F20   One brick thick

The code for the whole item is therefore F F10 F20 F10 F20.

It is plain that libraries constructed on this 'mix and match' approach will be much more compact and much more flexible than those constructed of whole descriptions, although the actual code constructed tends to be rather longer. In practice of course a library such as that indicated above would also require the addition of one further facet to deal with 'written short' items. This type of alphanumeric coding structure is widely used in many commercial systems, and the standard library published for use with SMM7 (HMSO 1988) follows this 'articulated phrase' approach, although with a rather different coding structure.

The coding structure used in the SMM7 Library of Standard Descriptions is an interesting variation on the technique discussed above. At the heart of the system is the concept of using the traditional quantity surveyor's shorthand description as the code instead of the usual meaningless alphanumeric string. This concept was first explored by the Ministry of Public Buildings and Works in the mid 1960s for use with the Enviro-computer system, and has subsequently been developed and refined within the Department of the Environment into the notation now used in the present SMM7 library.

The following is an example of the technique, and uses codes taken from the SMM7 Library of Standard Descriptions (the / characters simply indicate the end of each facet):

Coded item - ASP RF/SPEC A/RFG/W+300 FLAT

translates as follows:

ASP RF   Mastic asphalt roofing/insulation/finishes

SPEC A   Specification reference A

RFG   Roofing

W+300 FLAT   over 300 wide

It will be interesting to observe how widely the SMM7 library codes are used in practice. As we have already seen, the initial objective of this approach in the original Enviro system was to eliminate coding as a separate operation, but informal discussion with users both within the Department of the Environment and in private practice appear to show that this objective was not fully achieved, firstly because the standard codes became quite convoluted and, secondly, because every taker-off tends to develop his own set of 'pet' abbreviations with which he is comfortable and which he is reluctant to abandon.

All coded library systems need to make some provision for the coding of items not included in the library. Such items, commonly called 'rogues', are in practice encountered on almost every job, particularly those containing items of demolition or alteration. 'Rogue' items can be extremely time consuming and inconvenient to incorporate since, in addition to actually coding the item, the coder may also need to instruct the computer what the code for the rogue item actually means. This process can often involve both selecting a suitable unused or 'spare' code and also telling the computer whereabouts in the Bill the item is to be placed. The ease or otherwise with which rogue items can be accommodated can be a major factor in determining the cost effectiveness of any particular system.

Present-day solutions to the coding problem

The most commonly used approach to ease the coding problem centres around the use of VDU screens both for coding and for the input of the data. A number of systems use this approach.

In essence the method works by using the computer to display on the screen all of the descriptions and their associated codes stored in the library which are appropriate to a particular level of the item description, and the operator then chooses from the codes displayed. The system is in effect an automated library and is often an inverted tree structure through which the user is led step by step.

Early systems using this technique required the user to actually type in the chosen code on the keyboard, but more sophisticated and user friendly systems will allow the user to make a selection simply by 'pointing' to the appropriate item on the screen, either by using the cursor, a mouse, a light pen or some other electronic device. Such systems obviously hold out the possibility of direct entry of the dimensions by the taker-off via his own personal VDU, thus meeting in some degree the early hopes of eliminating the separate coding process. A printed copy of the dimensions and the descriptions chosen is usually generated simultaneously on a small printer attached to the VDU.

Such an approach can be very cost effective in that it eliminates the separate coding process, although it is apparent that, depending upon the response speed of the computer the taking off time may well be extended. The approach does however require that each taker-off has access to a VDU and this can itself present a problem since the taking off work-load in a typical office is not usually constant. Neither is it, in general, possible to even out the taking-off load since generally speaking the preparation of the Bills of Quantities is the last operation in the pre-tender phase and the taker-off is often working to a tight time-scale. The combination of these two factors means that, if the approach is to be successful then each taker-off must have his own terminal. This can, of course, not only make the initial cost of the system very high, particularly in an office with a large number of takers-off, but can also result in considerable under-use of terminals during slack taking-off periods.

An interesting alternative approach is the use of bar codes. This technique, used by at least one currently available system, uses specially printed libraries in which the code for each item is printed in the form of a bar code similar to that found on many tinned and packaged goods. The coder or taker-off therefore simply finds the description he requires in the library, and instead of writing down the description or typing it into a VDU, simply scans the bar code with a special pointer connected directly to the computer. One of the main advantages of this system over traditional coding techniques, as well as that of eliminating the traditional data entry process, is that the coding error rate is dramatically reduced.

Another alternative approach to solving the coding problem is the Phraseology Independent Billing System (PHIBS) developed jointly by the Architect's Department and the Computer Division of the Treasurer's Department of Derbyshire County Council with assistance from a number of others. This system has no library as such, the taker-off being completely free to use any terminology he wishes provided that the description is structured in levels in the way described earlier. The text is then entered into the computer by a clerk/typist exactly as written by the taker-off. Once a batch of data has been input to the machine the computer then scans the text at each level for 'keywords', from which it constructs an internal code. This 'hidden' code is then used both to collect like items together and to subsequently sort the data into Bill order.

The system also includes a number of other facilities to ease the taking-off process such as the use of 'ditto' for each facet of the description, easy duplication and re-use of previous descriptions with the option to make changes, the use of job-specific or global tables of abbreviated descriptions using 'shorthand' codes such as those described above and the facility to copy either single items or ranges of items from either previous dimensions or from previous Bills. The system therefore eliminates coding as a manual process and makes no additional demands upon the taker-off. There is also no need for each taker-off to have constant access to a VDU.

Electronic measurement tools

In addition to the 'basic' Bills of Quantities systems described above, a number of systems exist which also use the computer to assist with the measurement process, either by generating quantities for groups of items from one dimension (often termed automated measurement and discussed in more detail below), or by utilising some form of electronic measurement device.

Most common of these is the digitiser (see chapter 2), consisting of a flat board generally incorporating a matrix of wires and a pointing device of some kind. The board is able to detect the position of the pointer in both horizontal and vertical directions and to send this information to the computer as a series of X and Y co-ordinates usually relative to one of the corners of the board. Other technologies exist in addition to the wire matrix, for example the Techsonix system uses a digitiser equipped with ribbon microphones along the X and Y axes together with an ultra-sonic pointer. Digitiser tablets are available in a range of sizes from A3 to A0.

The digitiser itself is in concept a fairly simple device and it is easy to see how, given the X and Y co-ordinates of both ends of a straight line and some suitable software to handle the co-ordinate geometry involved, one could use the computer to calculate the length of the line. If the line were part of a scale drawing and the computer is told the correct scale then it is also easy to see how the computer could 'take-off' linear dimensions, and it is this simple concept which is at the heart of all systems using a digitised approach to measurement.

One of the major problems faced by the developers of systems of this type centred around the dimensional instability of the drawings. Stretching and shrinking of the paper often caused inaccurate measurement when using the scale provided by the operator. It is therefore now common for the computer itself to establish the true scale of the drawing in each of the X and Y directions. This is generally done by establishing a reference line, usually the longest dimensioned line, on each of the axes and telling the computer the intended length of each in 'real-world' dimensions via the keyboard. The lines are then measured by the computer and the software can thus establish the true scale of the drawing in each axis.

We have therefore seen how computers can be used to measure the length of straight lines, and it is obvious that given software only a little more complex the same technology can be used to measure the plan area of straight-sided shapes. In addition most digitisers will support a 'stream' mode of operation in which a continuous stream of X and Y co-ordinates is transmitted to the computer as the pointer is moved across the board. This facility thus allows the pointer to be used to trace curves, free and irregular shapes, and given again more complex software makes possible the calculation of both the length of curves and also the areas of free and irregular shapes. The application of such techniques to the measurement of, for example, floor and ceiling finishings and external works is obvious and the addition of further dimension information, often entered either through the keyboard or via a menu mounted on the digitiser board allows the automatic measurement from plans of wall areas, concrete volumes etc.

Some developers have constructed highly complex software for specialist measurement tasks such as the calculation of bulk earthworks volumes from digitised contour maps of existing and proposed ground surfaces. Such calculations are extremely tedious when done by hand and there is no doubt that the use of digitisers for this type of work saves enormous amounts of time and is very cost effective.

Most billing systems using this approach will use the digitiser board as an additional input device in conjunction with a VDU.

It should not be assumed however that digitisers offer a complete solution to the problem of measurement. Whilst, as shown above, the use of such techniques is very effective for certain types of work it is always as well to remember that, despite the machine's ability to compensate for the effects of the dimensional instability of paper, the accuracy of the measurement is only as good as:

(i)   the skill of the original draughstman and
(ii)   the skill of the digitiser operator particularly when following curves or the boundaries of irregular shapes

In addition it is obvious that the potential error margin will increase the smaller the scale of the drawing. It is plainly more difficult both to draw and to accurately trace shapes from drawings at a scale of 1:2500 than it is to follow similar lines on a drawing drawn at a scale of, say, 1:5, and it is plainly preferable in many cases to measure using figured dimensions when they are given. Remember that it is not for nothing that many architects and engineers add a note to their drawings warning of the dangers of using scaled dimensions!

Automated measurement

The use of the computer to 'automatically' measure a whole range of items from one code has its roots in the very beginnings of computer billing systems, and facilities of this type are described in several of the papers presented at both the 1967 and 1973 RICS conferences on computer billing systems. In essence the technique most commonly adopted uses the computer to store pre-measured quantities for parcels of work each of which is then given a unique code. The whole parcel may subsequently be included into a new scheme and multiplied as necessary simply by quoting the appropriate code and the 'number off', and thus considerable time can be saved where particular constructional details or component assemblies repeat from project to project. The most obvious examples occurred in the 1970s in the twin areas of local authority housing schemes and system building where component assemblies or even whole standard house types could be stored and recalled in this way. The technique has been given a variety of names by various system developers, (e.g. 'Blackbox', group quantities, unit quantities etc.); we shall use the term 'unit quantities'.

The technique is particularly important since it can also be used to form a useful link between computer billing systems and architects' computer aided design systems, and this is discussed further in chapter 12.

Unit quantities ~~*Databases*~~

One simple example of the use of unit quantities might be in the case of standard timber windows, which are commonly coded by the manufacturer and so identified in trade catalogues. A hypothetical example of such a window range is shown in figure 10.3, and is used here to indicate the way in which a unit quantity library could be constructed such that all of the measured items required for each type of window could be stored in the computer and associated with the relevant code.

Each window code would therefore need to generate the following items for inclusion in the Bill:

   (i)   supply and fixing of the window frame
  (ii)   glazing
 (iii)   painting internally and externally
 (iv)   bedding and pointing the frame.

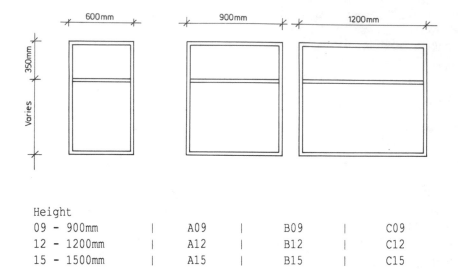

```
Height
09 - 900mm       |    A09    |    B09    |    C09
12 - 1200mm      |    A12    |    B12    |    C12
15 - 1500mm      |    A15    |    B15    |    C15
```

Notes
   (i)   Height of top light is always 350mm, bottom light varies
   (ii)   Windows may be glazed with either 4mm clear sheet glass (code
           C) or 4mm hammered obscure glass (code O)

Figure 10.3 Hypothetical range of timber windows

It is important to realise that the facilities available for this type of work differ greatly from one system to another. The example shown here is therefore not taken from any particular system but instead indicates the kind of facilities which have been offered in the past. The unit quantity library which might be prepared for the example given above is shown in figure 10.4.

```
Code    |   |     |   |Measured item
------------------------------------------------------------------
A09-(1) |   | 1 |   |Timb wdw/Sw/wdw & fr/ref A09 cramp fxg(2)
        |   |   |   |
A12-    |   | 1 |   |Timb wdw/Sw/wdw & fr/ref A12 cramp fxg
        |   |   |   |
A15-    |   | 1 |   |Timb wdw/Sw/wdw & fr/ref A15 cramp fxg
        |   |   |   |
B09-    |   | 1 |   |Timb wdw/Sw/wdw & fr/ref B09 cramp fxg
        |   |   |   |
B12-    |   | 1 |   |Timb wdw/Sw/wdw & fr/ref B12 cramp fxg
        |   |   |   |
B15-    |   | 1 |   |Timb wdw/Sw/wdw & fr/ref B15 cramp fxg
        |   |   |   |
C09-    |   | 1 |   |Timb wdw/Sw/wdw & fr/ref C09 cramp fxg
        |   |   |   |
```

```
C12-    |   . |   1   |       |Timb wdw/Sw/wdw & fr/ref C12 cramp fxg
        |     |       |       |
C15-    |     |   1   |       |Timb wdw/Sw/wdw & fr/ref C15 cramp fxg
        |     |       |       |
----(1) | 2/| *  |(3) |Timb wdw/mast/bed & ptg fr
        | 2/| ** |       |
        |     |       |       |
A--C(4) |     |  0.50|       |Gen glzg/stdd pln glas; 4mm clear sheet/
        |     |  0.25|       |wd puty/in s pane (nr.1)
        |     |       |       |
A--O    |     |  0.50|       |Gen glzg/stdd pln glas; 4mm hammered
        |     |  0.25|       |obsc./wd puty/in s pane (nr.1)
        |     |       |       |
B--C    |     |  0.80|       |Gen glzg/stdd pln glas; 4mm clear sheet/
        |     |  0.25|       |wd puty/in pane
        |     |       |       |
B--O    |     |  0.80|       |Gen glzg/stdd pln glas; 4mm hammered
        |     |  0.25|       |obsc./wd puty/in pane
        |     |       |       |
C--C    |     |  1.10|       |Gen glzg/stdd pln glas; 4mm clear sheet/
        |     |  0.25|       |wd puty/in pane
        |     |       |       |
C--O    |     |  1.10|       |Gen glzg/stdd pln glas; 4mm hammered
        |     |  0.25|       |obsc./wd puty/in pane
        |     |       |       |
A--(5)  |     |  0.50|       |Gen glzg/stdd pln glas; 4mm clear sheet/
        |     |   ** |(6) |wd puty/in pane
        |     |       |       |
A--C    |     |  0.50|       |Ddt. Ditto
        |     |  0.40|(7)|
        |     |       |       |
A--O    |     |  0.50|       |Gen glzg/stdd pln glas; 4mm hammered
        |     |   ** |       |obsc./wd puty/in pane
        |     |       |       |
A--O    |     |  0.50|       |Ddt. Ditto
        |     |  0.40|       |
        |     |       |       |
B--C    |     |  0.80|       |Gen glzg/stdd pln glas; 4mm clear sheet/
        |     |   ** |       |wd puty/in pane
        |     |       |       |
B--C    |     |  0.80|       |Ddt. Ditto
        |     |  0.40|       |
```

```
      |    |  .   |    |
B--O  |    | 0.80|    |Gen glzg/stdd pln glas; 4mm hammered
      |    |  **|     |obsc./wd puty/in pane
      |    |     |    |
B--O  |    | 0.80|    |Ddt. Ditto
      |    | 0.40|    |
      |    |     |    |
C--C  |    | 1.10|    |Gen glzg/stdd pln glas; 4mm clear sheet/
      |    |  **|     |wd puty/in pane
      |    |     |    |
C--C  |    | 1.10|    |Ddt. Ditto
      |    | 0.40|    |
      |    |     |    |
C--O  |    | 1.10|    |Gen glzg/stdd pln glas; 4mm hammered
      |    |  **|     |obsc./wd puty/in pane
      |    |     |    |
C--O  |    | 1.10|    |Ddt. Ditto
      |    | 0.40|    |
      |    |     |    |
----  |    |  *|      |Paint/pt wd/glzd wdw etc/g+300 m panes
      |    |  **| (8) |
      |    |     |    |
----  |    |  *|      |Paint e/pt wd/glzd wdw etc/g+300 m panes
      |    |  **|     |
      |    |     |    |
C12-  |(9) |  *|      |Ddt.Paint/pt wd/glzd wdw etc/g+300 m
      |    |  **|     |panes
      |    |     |    |
C12-  |    |  *|      |Ddt.Paint e/pt wd/glzd wdw etc/g+300 m
      |    |  **|     |panes
      |    |     |    |
C12-  |    |  *|      |Paint/pt wd/glzd wdw etc/g+300 l panes
      |    |  **|     |
      |    |     |    |
C12-  |    |  *|      |Paint e/pt wd/glzd wdw etc/g+300 l panes
      |    |  **|     |
      |    |     |    |
C15-  |    |  *|      |Ddt.Paint/pt wd/glzd wdw etc/g+300 m
      |    |  **|     |panes
      |    |     |    |
```

```
C15-    |    |    *|      |Ddt.Paint e/pt wd/glzd wdw etc/g+300 m
        |    |   **|      |panes
        |    |     |      |
C15-    |    |    *|      |Paint/pt wd/glzd wdw etc/g+300 l panes
        |    |   **|      |
        |    |     |      |
C15-    |    |    *|      |Paint e/pt wd/glzd wdw etc/g+300 l panes
        |    |    *|      |
```

Figure 10.4 Example unit quantity library

(1)   The size of the unit quantity library can be kept to a minimum by calling forward items using only parts of the total code. In this case the total number of windows in the range is nine and each window extracts five items. In addition each window can be glazed with either clear or obscure hammered glass. The code therefore needs to consist of the window reference and the type of glass, thus giving a total of $9 \times 5 \times 2 = 90$ separate items to be measured. Certain items however are only dependent upon a part of the code, for example the item for bedding and pointing is always required, and an item for the window frame is always required regardless of the type of glass. Using this technique only 38 items actually need to be measured to cover the entire range.

(2)   The abbreviations used are based on those included in SMM7 Library of Standard Descriptions.

(3)   Another technique which is sometimes used to minimise the size of the unit quantity library is to generate some dimensions automatically from the code via a look-up table. In this example one asterisk means that the dimension is generated from the first part of the code, and two asterisks means that the dimension is generated from the second part of the code. The code used here consists of three parts:

(i)   a letter denoting the width of the frame
(ii)   a two character number denoting the frame height
(iii) a single character denoting the type of glass

The different parts of the code are often referred to as 'parameters', and in this case look-up tables could be stored in the computer thus:

1st parameter (width)	2nd parameter (height)
A = 0.60	09 = 0.90
B = 0.90	12 = 1.20
C = 1.20	15 = 1.50

Thus when the computer finds a letter A as the first part of the code the * entry in the dimension column is replaced by 0.60, and so on.

(4)   This sequence of items measures the glazing to the top lights, which are always the same size regardless of the window height, hence only the width and glass type are significant.

(5)   These items measure the glazing to the bottom lights.

(6, 7) Here the dimension extracted from the second parameter of the code is multiplied by a given width to calculate the area of the bottom pane. Although not good conventional taking-off practice it again helps reduce the size of the unit quantity library to adopt the slightly unusual approach of measuring the area of the whole window and subsequently deducting the area occupied by the top light.

(8)   Here the dimensions for the painting items are both extracted from look up tables before being multiplied together in the usual way.

(9)   Although painting is required on all windows and is measured above, these two windows only are divided into large panes and thus call for special treatment. It is therefore necessary to deduct the painting already measured and add back the correct painting items

If we assume that a given project requires 10 Nr. type B12 windows glazed with clear glass and 2 Nr. type A09 windows glazed with obscure glass then the relevant items would be extracted from the unit quantity library, multiplied by the 'number off', and the dimensions shown in figure 10.5 would be merged with the traditionally measured work.

```
    |    |    |
 2/|  1  |   |Timb wdw/Sw/wdw & fr/ref A09 cramp fxg
    |    |    |
10/|  1  |   |Timb wdw/Sw/wdw & fr/ref B12 cramp fxg
    |    |    |
 2/| 0.60|   |Timb wdw/mast/bed & ptg fr
 2/| 0.90|   |
10/| 0.90|   |
10/| 1.20|   |
    |    |    |
 2/| 0.50|   |Gen glzg/stdd pln glas; 4mm hammered obsc./
   | 0.25|   |wd puty/in s panes (nr.2)
    |    |    |
 2/| 0.50|   |Gen glzg/stdd pln glas; 4mm hammered obsc./
   | 0.90|   |wd puty/in pane
    |    |    |
```

```
 2/| 0.50|    |Ddt. Ditto
    | 0.40|    |
    |     |    |
10/| 0.80|    |Gen glzg/stdd pln glas; 4mm clear sheet/
    | 0.25|    |wd puty/in pane
10/| 0.80|    |
    | 1.20|    |
    |     |    |
10/| 0.80|    |Ddt. Ditto
    | 0.40|    |
    |     |    |
 2/| 0.60|    |Paint/pt wd/glzd wdw etc/g+300 m panes
    | 0.90|    |
10/| 0.90|    |
    | 1.20|    |
    |     |    |
 2/| 0.60|    |Paint e/pt wd/glzd wdw etc/g+300 m panes
    | 0.90|    |
10/| 0.90|    |
    | 1.20|    |
    |     |    |
```

Figure 10.5 Dimensions selected from the unit quantity library

It can clearly be seen from the figure that the use of computerised techniques of this kind can be extremely cost effective where repetition occurs. It can however also be clearly seen from the above example that the preparation of comprehensive unit quantity libraries can be a very time consuming business, and it is therefore most important that one only considers the use of such methods where the extent of repetition is sufficient to justify the initial investment involved in establishing the library. One must also remember that, even with the best will in the world, architects and other designers seen incapable of leaving any standard detail unmodified for very long, and the ease with which unit quantity libraries of this type can be amended to take account of such changes will also be a crucial factor in their long-term cost effectiveness.

Other automated measurement techniques   *Spreadsheets*

An alternative approach to automated measurement is that used by the 'Calculix' system, reviewed in Hunt (1984). In this system the quantity surveyor, rather than measuring the building in the traditional way, 'describes' the building to the computer by working round each room wall by wall. The actual items and quantities are then extracted by the computer from the model thus created. The technique therefore requires a different approach to measurement but is claimed to be much more efficient than traditional methods once the taker-off has become accustomed to using the system. The approach again holds out the promise, in theory at least, of direct measurement from similar models created by architects using computer aided design systems.

It is also possible to use conventional spreadsheet software to assist in the measurement process quite independently of any bill production soft-

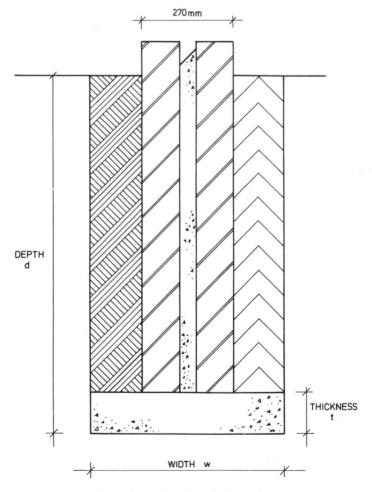

Figure 10.6 Simple strip foundation

ware and this can prove very cost effective in some circumstances. The approach is illustrated using the simple strip foundation shown in figure 10.6.

If the formulae required to calculate the quantities of work required for 1 metre run of the foundation were to be stored in a spreadsheet, then given the total trench depth, foundation concrete thickness, trench width and total length the computer will produce a schedule of all of the quantities involved.

Figure 10.7 shows a spreadsheet set up in this way, with the relevant formulae set up in cells F19 – F42. Figure 10.8 shows the input dialogue with the user after the spreadsheet borders have been removed and the sheet 'windowed' to display only the first thirteen lines. The relevant information is then entered into cells F10 – F13, and the resultant schedule of quantities is shown in figure 10.7.

```
  |   A   ||   B   ||   C   ||   D   ||   E   ||   F   ||   G
 1|
 2|                    SPREADSHEET MEASUREMENT EXAMPLE
 3|                    ================================
 4|
 5|                    Simple strip foundation
 6|                    -----------------------
 7|
 8|Enter the following information:-
 9|
10|         foundation depth (mm max 2000)          0
11|         trench width (mm)                        0
12|         concrete thickness (mm)                  0
13|         total length (m)                       .00
14|
15|Schedule of quantities
16|----------------------
17|
18|Excavate trench maximum depth not exceeding
19|     .00 m maximum depth                       .00 m3
20|
21|Level and compact bottom of excavation         .00 m2
22|
23|Earthwork support not exceeding 2.00 m
24|between opposing faces not exceeding
25|     .00 m maximum depth                       .00 m2
26|
27|Concrete in foundation in trench               .00 m3
28|
```

```
29|Half brick thick wall .00 m2
30|
31|Form cavity of hollow wall .00 m2
32|
33|Concrete filling to cavity of hollow wall .00 m3
34|
35|Backfill with excavated material .00 m3
36|
37|Backfill with hardcore .00 m3
38|
39|Remove surplus excavated material .00 m3
40|
41|Polymer damp proof course 110 mm wide
42|bedded in cement mortar (1:3) .00 m
```

Figure 10.7 Simple spreadsheet measurement

```
            SPREADSHEET MEASUREMENT EXAMPLE
            =================================


               Simple strip foundation
               -----------------------

Enter the following information:-

        foundation depth (mm max 2000)        900
        trench width (mm)                      750
        concrete thickness (mm)                225
        total length (m)                     27.50
```

Figure 10.8 Spreadsheet measurement – input dialogue

```
Schedule of quantities
----------------------


Excavate trench maximum depth not exceeding
    1.00 m maximum depth                       18.56 m3

Level and compact bottom of excavation         20.63 m2

Earthwork support not exceeding 2.00 m
between opposing faces not exceeding
    1.00 m maximum depth                       49.50 m2
```

Concrete in foundation in trench 4.64 m3

Half brick thick wall 45.38 m2

Form cavity of hollow wall 22.69 m2

Concrete filling to cavity of hollow wall 1.07 m3

Backfill with excavated material 4.46 m3

Backfill with hardcore 4.46 m3

Remove surplus excavated material 14.11 m3

Polymer damp proof course 110 mm wide
bedded in cement mortar (1:3) 55.00 m

Figure 10.9 Schedule of quantities

Data labelling

It is common for computerised Bill production systems to provide facilities for the basic information to be resorted into a number of different forms, for example it is common for tenders to be invited using a Bill arranged in SMM work section order whereas it may be more convenient for contract administration purposes if the Bill is subdivided by elements, work groups etc. It is also necessary to allocate items to particular sub-divisions if it is intended that an elemental cost analysis of any kind is to be produced from the priced Bill.

In order that these additional facilities may be exploited it is necessary for extra information to be input to the machine in addition to the description and dimension information discussed above. This additional information, sometimes referred to as 'data labels', is conventionally input in a coded form and the majority of systems include a separate 'library' of available types of sub-division together with the appropriate codes. A number of coding systems have been used in the past including CI/SfB, the Building Industry Code, the RICS Building Cost Information Service list of elements and sub-elements and many others.

The detailed facilities offered by individual systems do differ from one system to another, and some are more flexible than others, but typical systems have in the past allowed sub-division of the data by, for example:

house type
block – i.e. individual building within a total scheme
sub-block – a functional sub-divison of the above element
sub-element
location
SMM work section

Any or all labels are usually allowed in any one run, often in any combination; thus it is possible, assuming that the appropriate information has been coded, to produce for example a Bill sorted by block, sub-block and SMM work section for tender purposes and to subsequently resort the information into block, sub-block, element, and SMM work section form for use on site.

Civil engineering measurement

The measurement of civil engineering works poses its own quite distinct problems. Civil engineering works tend to be painted on a rather wider canvas than do building projects; the construction of a road, for example, tends to contain less of the fiddly detail than is usual on building projects of comparable or even much lesser value, and this is of course reflected in the rules for measurement of civil engineering work. In addition much civil engineering measurement is carried out by civil engineers rather than specialist quantity surveyors, and virtually all civil engineering work is remeasured as executed. The combination of these factors has tended to produce much simpler rules for the measurement of civil engineering works, culminating in the 2nd. edition of the Method of Measurement for Civil Engineering Works (CESMM2) which embodies not only the rules for measurement but also a full and mandatory standard library of descriptions. In addition of course the measurement of this type of work commonly involves much more involved calculation than does the measurement of building works. Such a situation is, of course, tailor made for computerisation.

Although most (if not all) of the billing systems designed for use on building projects could be fairly readily adapted for use on civil engineering works, they have tended in the main to be too complex for the type of measurement required, and neither have they provided suitable facilities to help ease the particular mathematical problems posed by civil engineering measurement. Consequently a number of computer systems have been developed specifically to cater for civil engineering works and these systems in turn have little or no application to building projects.

'Builders quantities' systems

As stated earlier, a number of the systems sometimes referred to as billing systems are in fact aimed predominantly at the smaller builder, whose needs are for a system enabling him to easily produce his own quantities for plan and specification work. Since the eventual aim of such systems is the production of an estimate for a project rather than the production of a Bill of Quantities they therefore tend to include only rudimentary billing facilities but quite complex estimating and pricing routines. They tend therefore, in the main, not to be suitable for use by the quantity surveyor in the production of bills of quantities in accordance with the Standard Method of Measurement, but they can however be of use in other areas of work, in particular for approximate estimating.

References

Alvey R.J. (1976) *Computers in quantity surveying* Macmillan

Dent C. (1964) *Quantity surveying by computer* Oxford University Press

Hunt G. (1984) 'Now you can measure your modules' *Chartered Quantity Surveyor* January 1984 p. 219

Hunt G. (1985) 'The all-singing all-dancing system?' *Chartered Quantity Surveyor* January 1985 p. 213

HMSO (1988) *SMM7 Library of Standard Descriptions* HMSO

RICS (1961) 'The use of computers for working up' *Chartered Surveyor* April 1961 pp. 561–563

Sweet (1978) *Concepts in quantity surveying* Cyril Sweet and Partners publicity material

11 Computers for Post Contract Work

Objectives

At the end of this chapter you will be able to:

- Comment on the general use of computers in post contract work.
- Discuss the factors affecting the re-use of bill production data for post contract work and the establishment of a comprehensive integrated project data base.
- Discuss the advantages and disadvantages of the use of portable computers on site

Computers in post contract work

Previous chapters have examined the various ways in which computers may be used by the quantity surveyor in his professional role both during the inception and feasibility stage of a project and also to aid in the production of contract documentation, particularly the preparation of Bills of Quantity. This chapter examines the use of the computer during the post contract phase of a project.

In some ways this is by far the most difficult area of the quantity surveyor's work to explore from the point of view of computer usage, since although the use of computers during this stage is quite common the precise use to which they may be put will depend to a large extent upon the post contract arrangements for the particular project and the extent to which the quantity surveyor is involved in areas such as project management. It is therefore obvious that whilst the quantity surveyor may have some specific and particular needs he is also in many instances likely to make use of systems more often considered the responsibility of the contractor or the engineer. Indeed he may well, in some cases, not only use the software but also data created by some other member of the construction team. The position is also rather special for the quantity surveyor employed by a contractor. In this case the quantity surveyor is likely to be less involved in the formal administration of the Contract, but much more concerned with factors such as the administration of nominated and domestic sub-contractors and the profitability of the project from his employer's point of view. He may well therefore use computers, indeed may be deluged with computer printout, but the systems with which he is concerned are likely to be those to do with the management of the building company itself. A study of systems of this type more rightly falls within the province of building management, and is not therefore included here. This chapter will instead concentrate on those computer systems which might be used by the quantity surveyor acting as consultant to the employer, specifically in the areas of contract administration and financial management.

Contract administration and financial management

Although it is probably true that the automatic production of the Final Account by computer is not yet feasible, mainly due to the amount of human interaction and negotiation involved between the parties to the contract, nonetheless knowledgeable commentators have long considered contract administration and financial management to be among the most fertile areas for the application of computers to quantity surveying. Gordon Hunt for example wrote in 1981:

> It is my personal view that microcomputers prove to be at their most cost effective in a quantity surveying office when used for post contract applications.
>
> (Hunt 1981a)

and Gordon Darby, well known pioneer of the use of microcomputers by quantity surveyors is reported as saying:

> Post contract operations are the most fruitful areas for micros. A large reduction in the operating time on, say, valuations allows time for that poor relation the final account under optimum conditions – namely while the job is still in progress.
>
> (Hunt 1981b)

The contract administration and financial management functions to which microcomputers have most often been applied include:

- interim valuations
- cost monitoring and progress reports
- calculation of fluctuations
- cash flow prediction
- prediction of 'out-turn' costs
- claims management

Note that use of the computer for cost analysis is discussed in chapter 9 and is therefore excluded here.

Interim valuations

The use of computers for the working up of interim valuations has been pursued for some considerable time and a number of companies market programs of this type, either as stand-alone programs or as modules of an integrated suite.

There is a wide range of approaches to the problem. At one extreme some surveyors have found it most cost effective to use a combination of word processing and spreadsheet software to simply calculate and print the valuation statement complete with notifications to nominated sub-contractors, whilst at the other end of the scale one can conceive of systems in which the quantity surveyor actually prepares the valuation at a screen on site, extracting items from a priced Bill held on-line, and in which the computer automatically performs all of the calculations and prepares the relevant documentation. It is perhaps in this area that the use of portable computers or site-based computer terminals linked to a remote central system is likely to expand rapidly in the future.

Much use has been made of microcomputers for so called 'tick-sheet' valuations, where the quantity surveyor prepares his valuation using some form of computer generated chart upon which are recorded all of the details of work completed, variations etc. The method is particularly suited to work with a high degree of repetition such as housing, and examples of systems of this type are described in Hunt (1981b) and Belcher (1983). An example of a spreadsheet representation of the same problem is given in Hawkins and Massey (1988).

Cost monitoring and progress reports

It is important that Employers are kept aware of changes in the estimated cost of a project throughout the progress of the work, and this is conventionally done by providing the Employer with a series of financial statements showing the effect of any variations at regular intervals as work progresses. Whilst most of the integrated systems will provide for such a statement to be produced at the touch of a button, it is also possible to use spreadsheet software to create and maintain statements of this type.

Figure 11.1 shows a 'blank' spreadsheet of this type created using Supercalc 2 which allows variations to be listed. In this example each

```
 | A ||   B   ||     C     ||      D    ||E||   F   ||   G   |
 1|
 2|PROJECT:
 3|==========================================================
 4|
 5|Tender value:          .00
 6|=========================
 7|
 8|Date:00/00/00
 9|============
10|
11|List of variations and predicted final cost
12|===========================================
13|
14|Arch. inst.   Description                      Add    Omit
15|----------------------------------------------------------
16|
17|
18|Predicted final cost #            .00
19|
20|
```

Figure 11.1 Example of use of spreadsheet for cost monitoring

variation is recorded by simply inserting an extra row into the sheet after line 16, and cell D18 contains a formula which allows the tender value from cell C5 to be adjusted by the sum of the values stored in columns F16-F17 and G16-G17. As additional rows are inserted the spreadsheet software itself adjusts this formula so that the amount given as 'predicted final cost' is always the initial tender sum adjusted by the amount of total additions and omissions from columns F and G. An example of the spreadsheet in use, with the borders removed, is shown in figure 11.2.

Calculation of fluctuations

Most fluctuating price contracts now use one or other of the 'formula' methods for the calculation of fluctuations. These methods rely on the use of indices representing the average movement of prices for particular types of work, and the most popular system for building works is the so-called NEDO formula using indices prepared and published by central government. The operation of this system is described in PSA (1977) and, whilst

```
PROJECT:        Blanktown Primary School
================================================================

Tender value: £     450102.66
=============================

Date:17/09/88
=============

List of variations and predicted final cost
============================================

Arch. inst.    Description                      Add      Omit
----------------------------------------------------------------
    1          Take possession of site         .00       .00
    2          Steel frame P.C.            12050.63  10000.00
    3          Revision to foundations     1250.50       .00
    4          Heating P.C.               15210.00  17500.00
    5          Omit provl.sums for rock        .00   2500.00
    6          Amend spec for facings       395.00       .00
    7          Additional rooflights       1500.00       .00
    8          Electrical P.C.            11472.36  12500.00

Predicted final cost          £     449481.15
```

Figure 11.2 Example of use of spreadsheet for cost monitoring

the method itself is quite straightforward, the lengthy calculations involved mean that the calculation of fluctuations in this way is well suited to the use of computers. Accordingly many organisations have developed programs specifically for this task.

The calculation has also been modelled using spreadsheets, and two examples are given in Hawkins and Massey (1988).

Cash flow prediction

Cash flow essentially defines the pattern of expenditure on a building project, and is therefore vitally important both to the contractor and to the employer. Traditional methods of modelling cash flow relied upon calculations based on the contractor's construction programme, and many of the computer systems developed for project management continue to calculate cash flow on this basis.

It is however possible to predict cash flow patterns for a building project independently of the contractor's programme using a method initially developed by the Department of Health and Social Security and first described in Hudson (1978). The method uses a series of 'S' curves to represent expenditure on a building project over time, a relationship which had previously been recognised but not precisely analysed. The major contribution of the DHSS work was the establishment of a precise mathematical relationship between the variables involved, and the derivation of a mathematical expression in the form of an equation and a table of parametric values for projects of differing size. Whilst the original paper presented by the DHSS team related purely to health buildings subsequent unpublished empirical work appears to show that the results are equally valid for other types of building. A spreadsheet representation of the problem is again included in Hawkins and Massey (1988).

One further advantage of the DHSS cash flow modelling technique is that, in addition to generating cash flow forecasts, the same algorithm may be used, given past interim valuation amounts, to predict the contract period. This feature is obviously very useful in cases where the contractor appears to be falling behind programme.

Prediction of out-turn costs

Although, as stated earlier, it is common practice for clients to be provided with financial progress reports during the post contract stage of a project, such reports will often only consider the addition and omission of variations from the tender value, and will make little or no attempt to forecast future fluctuations. Whilst this approach is acceptable for contracts of short duration in times of fairly stable prices, the same may not be true for projects with an extended contract period or in times of high or rising inflation. In these circumstances Employers may be much more interested in the predicted total cost of the scheme, including fluctuations; the so-called 'out-turn' cost.

Various statistical techniques can be employed which use the trends revealed by a study of tables of past cost indices to attempt to predict future cost trends, and simple BASIC programs using these methods have been developed by a number of organisations for their own private use.

'Stand-alone' or integrated systems?

It should be obvious from the above that there are essentially two approaches to the use of computers for post contract work in the areas of contract administration and financial management.

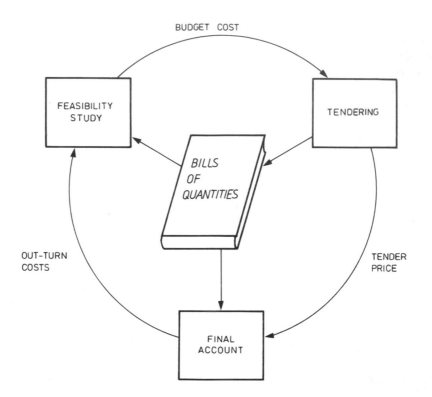

Figure 11.3 A cyclical view of construction cost monitoring

On the one hand lies what might be called the traditional 'all-singing, all-dancing' approach. This approach considers that since the process of financial management of building contracts tends to be essentially cyclical as shown in figure 11.3, centred on the use of cost data extracted from priced Bills of Quantities, then computer systems should be linked together to form integrated suites to facilitate this process. Such a philosophy generally sees the central core of the system as an integrated database of information based on the priced tender Bill. The post contract module of such a system might typically provide facilities to handle:

- variations
- interim valuations
- cost monitoring and progress reports
- payment notifications to nominate sub-contractors
- formula fluctuations
- cash flow prediction

A diagrammatic representation of such a system is shown in figure 11.4.

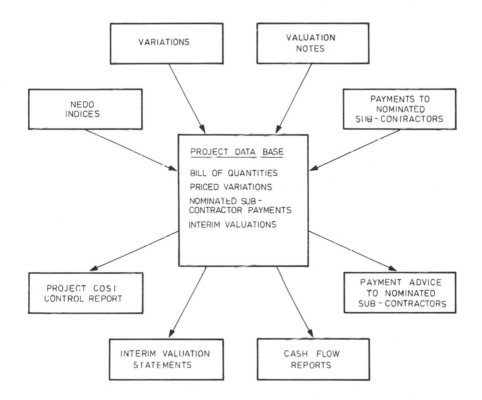

Figure 11.4 An integrated aproach to post contract work

Suites of this type are usually menu-driven via a VDU screen and their operation is quite straightforward. They do however tend to be rather expensive and the cost effectiveness of such systems must be carefully researched.

On the other hand, however, it is, as illustrated earlier, perfectly possible to use software tools such as spreadsheets or even to write small self-contained programs in a simple language such as BASIC to deal with specific post contract tasks on a 'stand-alone' basis. The use of such tools can be extremely cost effective, but one should always be conscious of the factors discussed earlier in chapter 7.

The most important difference between the 'stand-alone' approach and the integrated database concept described earlier is that in the latter case, because all of the information is stored in one central set of files, then the input of any new data via any of the routes shown in figure 11.4 will immediately be reflected in all of the relevant outputs. Hence a change in, for example, the estimated value of an Architect's Instruction will automatically be reflected in reports such as those for cash flow monitoring etc.

A number of firms market integrated post contract suites of the type referred to above, but it would be quite possible for the quantity surveyor to develop his own integrated system using data manipulation tools such as dBase or Lotus 123. Note however that both the difficulty and time scale of such development is usually grossly under-estimated and the comments made in Chapter 7 regarding the development of systems in-house apply particularly to this type of work.

The evaluation of contractual claims

As pressure from developers and building owners increases to reduce the time available for pre-contract design and construction, so the planning and control of construction projects becomes more critical, and the effect of changes to the project either during the design or the construction phases becomes more important in terms of both cost and time. Contractors are now turning more and more towards computerised aids to project planning in an attempt to control both time and cost within the more stringent contractual conditions now imposed upon them. One predictable result of this situation is an increase in claims by contractors, either in respect of additional costs or for an extension to the contract period, and many of these claims are now supported by reams of computer print-out generated from the contractors management systems.

Under the JCT Standard Form of Building Contract both the architect and the quantity surveyor have a role to play in the granting of extensions to the contract period and in the agreement of any additional monies paid to the contractor, and this form of contract, in common with a number of others, now requires the contractor to produce and maintain a 'master programme' in order that the consultants might be able more clearly to assess the true effect of any delay or disruption which may occur. Whilst this is a welcome first step, it is of limited value since planning of the works remains the contractor's responsibility and the contractor is not required to divulge the information on which his plan is based. It therefore follows that, in the majority of cases, the consultants involved can only form very subjective judgements about the accuracy and correctness of the plan put forward by the contractor. In addition most consultant architects and quantity surveyors do not clearly understand the workings of computer based planning packages, and it is therefore very difficult, once some delay or disruption occurs, to argue convincingly against claims submitted by the contractor on the basis of a variance with his original plan, particularly so when the plan has been generated from a computer based project management and planning package.

In an attempt to ease this situation some organisations responsible for large projects now not only require the contractor to prepare a master programme, but also require him to plan the project using a specified computer based project management system in which the consultants have a degree of expertise. This method of working thus enables the consultant to check rather more thoroughly the contractor's progress against the plan, to evaluate much more readily the time consequences of a change to the plan, and even to indulge in 'what-if' simulations in order to predict the best ways in which the required changes can be implemented.

This process has become known as 'claims management', and the use of computer based techniques such as those indicated above appears likely to increase in the near future.

A more comprehensive discussion of the use of project planning and control systems by the quantity surveyor is given in chapter 13.

Portable and site-based computers

Recent developments in computer hardware have made possible an increasingly wide range of computer equipment which is rugged enough for use on site. Site based computer equipment has been in use by some of the larger building contractors for some time, particularly on large sites, and may take the form either of computer terminals linked to a remote mainframe computer, or, increasingly more likely, site based micro or minicomputers linked to the company mainframe. Such systems can be used for a wide variety of construction management tasks including, among others, ordering and logging of materials, cost and bonus calculations, cash flow forecasts, cost/value reconciliation exercises and construction planning using software such as that considered for project management in chapter 13. Whilst such systems have always been useful to the contractor's surveyor, it is only recently, with the increasing use of alternative forms of procurement such as management contracts where the consultants and the contractor work much more closely together, that the consultant quantity surveyor has been allowed access to such systems.

Another development which has great potential for future use is the wide range of portable computers now available. Until comparatively recently such machines had limited memory and were largely used in industry as 'data loggers', collecting information for subsequent transmission to a larger computer for subsequent processing. Typical examples are in the retail industry for stock control, and in land surveying where such machines are often used in conjunction with electronic theodolites to collect survey data for later processing by an office based survey plotting system, but such machines are now sufficiently powerful for surveyors to begin to use them for actually processing data on site. The potential uses, particularly for interim valuations and site measurement, are plain to see.

References

Belcher R. (1983) 'Speeding housing estate valuations' *Chartered Quantity Surveyor* June 1983 pp. 417–421

Hawkins P. and Massey R. (1988) *Spreadsheet examples* Department of Surveying, Trent Polytechnic

Hudson K.W. (1978) 'DHSS expenditure forecasting method' *Chartered Surveyor Building and Quantity Surveying Quarterly* Spring 1978

Hunt G. (1981a) 'Micronotes – finding the data' *Chartered Quantity Surveyor* February 1981 p. 263

Hunt G. (1981b) 'Micronotes – micros at the post contract stage' *Chartered Quantity Surveyor* March 1981 p. 285

PSA (1977) *Price adjustment formulae for building contracts: Guide to the application and procedure* HMSO

12 Quantity Surveyors and Computer Aided Design

Objectives

At the end of this chapter you will be able to:

- Discuss the production of quantities directly from a computer aided design system in an integrated practice.
- Comment on the possibilities for the extraction of data from the architect's project model by other private practice quantity surveyors.
- Discuss the problems which govern the exchange of data between different computer systems.
- Comment on the legal and economic issues involved in the use of the architect's data by the quantity surveyor.

CAD – some general considerations

This chapter is concerned with the use of computers for design and draughting within the building industry, and the possible effects that a wider spread of such systems might have upon the work of the quantity surveyor.

Computers have been used to aid the production of drawings for many years, especially in the engineering disciplines, and it is therefore perhaps a little surprising that, as recently as May 1987, Edgill and Atkin, commenting upon a project to investigate the opportunities such systems might hold for quantity surveyors, stated that:

...it was evident that many misconceptions (about computer aided design) were held by quantity surveyors. Whatever these amounted to, it was clear that CAD was not well understood.

(Edgill and Atkin 1987)

It is therefore obviously necessary to examine a little of the background of computer aided design before attempting any kind of analysis of the effects that the use of such systems might have on the quantity surveyor.

CAD – what is it?

One of the problems about CAD is that this particular set of initials has at least two generally accepted meanings. CAD may, in some circumstances, mean computer aided *design*, where the computer is used to actually assist in the design process, but the same initials may equally well be used to refer to computer aided *draughting*, where the computer is merely used as a tool to produce working drawings. In an attempt to ease the confusion some commentators refer to computer aided architectural design (CAAD), whilst others prefer CADD (computer aided design and draughting). The term CAD is used here to denote computer aided design.

Computers have been used to aid the engineering design process for some 25 years, and their use in areas such the car and aeroplane manufacturing industries is well known. In industries such as these links have long been formed between the computers used for design work and those used to control the machines which actually make the parts from which the final product is assembled; thus CAD/CAM (computer aided design/ computer aided manufacturing) is yet another acronym which the use of computers has introduced to the vocabulary of the modern industrialist.

Almost from the very beginning engineering computer aided design systems incorporated facilities to enable the computer to generate not only drawings and instructions to drive machine tools but also to produce a 'bill of materials', a list of components required to produce the final composite assembly. The potential application of this technique to construction was quickly recognised in theory but proved rather more difficult to achieve in practice.

The amount of computing power required to 'model' designs for cars and aeroplanes was huge, and more rather than less was required to model large buildings. In addition companies involved in producing cars, aeroplanes and similar products tend to be very large, dealing in general with sizeable production runs of a given product; construction on the other hand tends to be a much more 'one-off' affair and most architectural practices of the time were, with a few notable exceptions, unable to afford the the hardware required. It therefore tended to be in the large local authorities, largely on the back of the very large public sector building programmes of the early 1970s, that computer aided architectural design began to blossom. Similar developments had already taken place in civil and structural engineering with computers being used to aid the design of projects such as the St Lawrence Seaway and the Sydney Opera House, and many widely used programs were developed for highway design, the design of reinforced concrete and steel structures etc.

Probably the earliest comprehensive published account of computer aided architectural design was Campion (1968), but by the mid- to late-1970s a number of computer aided design systems were in regular use;

Madden (1973) for example describes a system which had been in use in West Sussex County Council since 1968, Carter (1973a-d), in a series of four articles explored the application of computers in architecture, Maver (1978) catalogues a number of contemporary CAD systems, and Daniel (1979) and Hawkins and Davidson (1979) both describe ways in which quantities could be extracted from such systems.

As with most other applications of computers a widespread interest in the techniques really began with the general introduction of low cost microcomputers during the late 1970s since which time a number of comparatively low cost CAD systems have been developed.

Types of CAD system

There are essentially two types of system in common use. The majority of the cheaper systems, usually based on small computers, will be described as 2D (two-dimensional) systems, and are often little more than automated draughting tools. They will generally permit the creation of working drawings in a flat (i.e. two-dimensional) plane, often allowing commonly used shapes or symbols to be defined, stored in a library and subsequently retrieved and placed in a drawing, and will also provide functions to allow shapes to be scaled, deformed or rotated in various ways.

In general however each drawing is a separate entity in its own right and there is no transfer of information between the various drawings which make up a project, hence if changes are made to one drawing they will not automatically be reflected in other drawings for the same project.

Some two-dimensional systems do permit shapes to be given the additional attribute of a third dimension, thus allowing some limited facilities for the production of, for example wire-frame perspectives. Such systems are commonly known as 2.5D systems, but the facilities offered vary from system to system. It is therefore very difficult to define precisely what a 2.5D system actually is.

The most sophisticated systems, in my view the only ones which can rightly be called computer aided design systems, are those offering a true three-dimensional modelling capability. Such systems are obviously known as 3D systems. The most common approach for systems of this type is for individual components to be defined to the computer in terms of plan, front elevation and side elevation views, generally using the projection of the object onto the top, front and side of an enclosing box. The computer is then instructed as to the position of the component in three dimensions within the building, and by this means a complete 'model' of the proposed building is constructed within the computer's memory. With systems of this type therefore individual project drawings are generated by asking the computer to view the model from the desired direction. 'Layered' drawings can be produced by instructing the machine only to look at particular groups of components; thus it is possible to generate, for example, a plan view of a building showing only the structural walls, as well as a complete floor plan showing all of the features stored.

The use of 3D techniques has many advantages over 2D or 2.5D systems, some of the most significant being:

(i)   Once the original data are input views may be produced at will at any level either in plan, elevation or section and to any scale.

(ii)   Perspective, orthographic or isometric projections may be generated on demand from any viewpoint and with hidden lines removed.

(iii)   A change in the shape or position of any of the components will instantly be reflected in any drawings subsequently produced.

It is therefore obvious that 3D systems are much more flexible than their 2D or 2.5D cousins; they are however, in general, much more expensive, and require greater computer power to work effectively.

Most of the modern generation of 3D systems allow views to be displayed in colour on a suitable high resolution monitor, and this can be of great benefit to the architect in the initial design stages of a project, for presentation to a client, or to assist with the obtaining of planning approval for controversial sites. Techniques have been developed whereby computer generated perspectives have been combined with photographs of the street-scape in order to enable clients and planners to visualise the environmental effects of a new building, as well as techniques using a series of internal perspectives edited onto video tape giving an illusion of 'walking through' the computer model. There is no doubt that this 'public relations' aspect of CAD will assume increasing importance in the future, and some researchers are already speculating on the development of systems using laser-generated, three-dimensional holographic representations of the computer model. Such visions may appear futuristic and fanciful, but then, ten years ago, so did the concept of a lap-top computer and a pocket-sized television!

CAD and the quantity surveyor

From the very beginning the use of computer aided design systems has had a potential impact on the work of the quantity surveyor, primarily in the areas of measurement and initial cost advice.

As regards measurement, we have already seen that CAD systems in engineering produce bills of materials almost as a by-product, and the construction of a building was perceived to be, in essence, no different from the construction of an aeroplane. There seemed therefore no obvious reason why Bills of Quantities should not be extracted from the CAD model in the same way.

The impact upon the extent of the quantity surveyor's role in giving initial cost advice is equally obvious since one of the primary reasons for architects using CAD systems in the first place was to enable a wider range of options to be examined and evaluated within the same time scale as traditional methods.

We have also seen that the early building CAD systems were largely developed within integrated practices; quantity surveyors were therefore on hand and could collaborate actively in the system development. Problems of data transfer between one system and another therefore tended to be minimal.

Automatic measurement from CAD models

We have seen above that the majority of 3D CAD modelling systems, and a number of 2D and 2.5D systems, operate through the use of 'components' defined in a library held in the computer. A component might be a discrete unit, for example a window, a door or a sanitary fitting with fixed dimensions, or alternatively a 'stretchable' component such as an area of floor slab or an area of brick wall. Components may also be composites formed from combinations of other components, for example a standard house type, and all components are generally referenced by some sort of code.

This technique has much in common with the 'unit quantity' techniques already in use in quantity surveyors' billing systems and described earlier (chapter 9), and since the CAD systems already possess the ability to 'count' the number of each type of component used in a model the integration of CAD and quantity surveyors' billing systems was, in a number of cases, successfully exploited. Considerable success was achieved in the 1970s particularly in the local authority sector, in West Sussex, Derbyshire and Clwyd County Councils among others, and a typical example is described in Daniel (1979). More recent work using the same techniques is described by Wager and Wilson (1986), whilst a rather different perspective on the same problem envisaging the use of data extracted directly from a CAD model and subsequently converted to SMM form via a spreadsheet is briefly described in Curran (1987).

Cost advice

The other major area of influence on the quantity surveyor's role lies in the provision of initial cost advice for a number of different options on a given scheme, and this problem was historically solved by including costs with the graphical description of the component stored in the CAD system library. Since, as we have already seen, the CAD system itself was able to total the numbers of each component used in any particular model, the generation of project cost became almost a trivial matter which simply required the quantity surveyor to update the computer forecast for time, location and local difficulty. The evaluation of alternatives during the development of the design thus became much more straightforward.

Some system developers exploited this technique in other directions, adding additional data to the component description such as heat loss co-efficients or cost in use information. The computer was then able to generate total heat losses, cost in use reports etc. An account of such a system is given in Jelly (1977).

Transfer of data between computer systems

It has already been noted (chapter 2) that grave problems arise when attempting to transfer data from one computer system to another, and this is particularly true where CAD systems are concerned. Whilst it has already been noted that data were transferred between CAD and quantity surveyors' billing systems, this transfer in general took place among machines of the same type, and generally involved the output of specially processed data from one machine onto some physical medium, often punched cards, which could subsequently be read back into another machine. This method of transfer is extremely expensive and inefficient in that it requires a special program to convert data from the host machine into a suitable form for processing by the target system. Add to this the fact that, on any particular project, data might also need to be exchanged between the architect and quantity surveyor and the services and structural engineers and the number of permutations, and hence the number of special translation programs required becomes unmanageable.

Wix and McLelland (1986) conducted a study of the problem, and report on the development of a data exchange standard for graphics systems called the Initial Graphics Exchange Standard (IGES). The central concept underlying IGES is the establishment of a standard format to which all graphics data should be converted. Hence if an architect with one CAD system wished to transfer some data to an engineer with another system then the architect would simply instruct his computer to output the data in IGES format and the engineer would instruct his system to expect the input in the same form. Each separate type of CAD system thus only needs to provide one output processor and one input processor to be able to communicate with all other IGES systems. IGES or systems like it could therefore, in the future, provide a common interchange format for data transfer not only among CAD systems but also between CAD systems and quantity surveying packages, project management systems and the like.

Other attempts at standardisation of format and equipment are described in RIB E.V. (1982) and CICA (1982).

Legal and economic issues

It has been shown above that a considerable amount of information useful to the quantity surveyor can already be extracted from CAD systems, in particular measurement and cost information, and there have been those who suggest that this might serve to bring the two professions closer together.

Whilst this may be very welcome within the context of an integrated practice, problems of responsibility for the accuracy and completeness of the information produced may occur where more traditional consultancy relationships apply. It is for example very easy to imagine a scenario in which a quantity surveying practice prepares an early estimate of the cost of a project using quantity or even cost data extracted from an architect's CAD system, but what would be the consequences if the estimate proved to be wildly inaccurate because the original information was incorrect? The answer is surely that the quantity surveyor, since he is responsible for the estimate and is presumably being paid a fee for producing it, must carry the responsibility for the error, and this leads one to the view that the quantity surveyor would need to check very carefully any information provided by other consultants. Such checking could well, of course, take longer and be more costly than preparing the same information manually in the first place, but it is a well recognised phenomenon that people are likely to accept computer produced information at face value, and it is interesting to speculate as to how many quantity surveyors would be prepared to take the risk.

There are also economic factors to consider. Again the problem is less acute within an integrated practice, but where a number of independent consultants are concerned one can easily imagine architects' reluctance to provide the quantity surveyor with quantity or cost information free of charge.

Some have speculated that one way in which the above problems might be overcome would be for the quantity surveyors themselves to invest in CAD systems, but this appears at present to be unlikely at least on a large scale. Whatever the outcome it is clear that there are influences here which might well act against the wider dissemination of information from CAD systems in the immediate future.

Benefits and disadvantages to the quantity surveyor

The use of CAD systems has proved both good and bad from the quantity surveyor's point of view. In terms of benefits the automatic generation of quantities and cost information has undoubtedly in many cases proved most helpful, saving both time and cost and providing the client with better value for his money.

On the other hand however there have been some disadvantages:

(i)   The creation of the unit quantity libraries, described in chapter 9, which are necessary to take advantage of the automatic measurement facilities discussed above is very time consuming and very costly. The quantity surveyor needs to be assured of a number of uses if the initial investment is to be worthwhile. It is not therefore, in general, worth doing for a 'one-off' scheme, but only where the same components or constructional details are to be re-used as 'standards' on several projects. This method tends therefore to be much more attractive in the context of an integrated practice than in the case of a consultant quantity surveyor who may only work occasionally with a particular architect. It can however work well in the case of a programme of similar projects and a good example is the redevelopment of petrol filling stations by Mobil Oil described in Wager and Wilson (1987).

(ii)   Once the components have been defined and stored in the CAD system library the architect must be prepared to leave them unchanged as far as possible. This seems self-evident, and indeed one might consider that the ability to recall tried and tested constructional details might be one very good reason for having a CAD system in the first place. It appears however that this is not the case. A major survey of communications in the construction industry conducted in 1985/86 found that:

> One surprising finding which emerged was how little CAD systems seem to be used for producing standard details in architects' offices... In practice we found that this hardly ever happened although in the case of one architectural practice there had been a considerable investment creating such a library. However when it came to to using the library it was found that architects preferred to work out their own details for a job rather than resorting to those already available.
>
> (Day, Faulkner and Happold 1986:p. 20)

> Whilst changes made to a component may be minor in graphical terms, perhaps a change to a dimension, the effect upon the quantity surveyor's pre-measured quantities can be catastrophic!

(iii) Even worse than (ii) above, although in a way related to it, is the tendency shown by some architects to manually alter drawings produced by a CAD system. Again the architect will often see such changes as trivial but the possible effect upon pre-measured quantities is again obvious. Manual amendment of computer generated quantities to take account of such changes is usually very difficult and the modification and adjustment of such quantities may take longer than measuring from scratch by manual methods.

(iv) The information flow from the architect may become disjointed by the use of CAD. Day, Faulkner and Happold (1986) found that:

> Because a whole set of drawings can be plotted relatively quickly, there is a tendency to leave the plotting until immediately before the due date for the information in order to ensure that all amendments are incorporated.

and later:

> ...it appears that where there is the potential to issue a 'perfect' drawing there is much greater reluctance to issue any drawing until that perfect drawing is available.

The future impact on the quantity surveyor

The probable future impact of an increase in the use of CAD techniques on the role of the quantity surveyor is very hard to predict. On the one hand Bruce Graham, senior architect with the London office of Skidmore, Owings, Merrill is reported as saying that:

> The quantity surveyor is not necessary with the computer. The computer measures the quantities much more accurately than a quantity surveyor.

whereas on the other hand Edgill and Atkin (1987) assert that:

> It (CAD) will only present problems if quantity surveyors fail to recognise the impact it will have on present methods of working. CAD is only likely to be a threat if it is perceived to be one, with little or no attempt being made to investigate its positive aspects.

The diversity of these two views shows neatly the difference of opinion which presently exists. Whilst it is tempting to disregard Graham's view as the opinion of one who apparently has only the sketchiest of notions about what a quantity surveyor does, there is really little comfort to be gained from Edgill and Atkin's view that CAD is only a threat if it is perceived to be one.

Clearly the spread of powerful low cost CAD systems will influence dramatically the role of the quantity surveyor, and it is therefore, by some, perceived to be a threat. Brandon (1983) for example says:

> For the first time in the history of mankind, technology has produced a machine, the computer, which will not only enhance human abilities in certain areas but also replace them in a more efficient manner. Measurement as a technique (not only quantity surveying measurement) is threatened because, by its very nature, it is usually an unambiguous process which can be wholly described in a logical manner and which relies heavily on another process, design, planning or creation.

It is, I believe, inevitable that some changes will take place in the quantity surveyor's role; the question is no longer whether changes will occur but when will the changes occur and what will the scope of them be.

The period since 1983 has already seen evidence of fundamental changes; quantity surveyors are concentrating less on their historical role as measurers and valuers and are instead promoting much more aggressively the image of the quantity surveyor as manager and facilitator of the building procurement process. Such a movement is obviously totally consistent with the pressure which a spread of CAD activity would impose, and those quantity surveyors who are prepared to make the required role shift will, I believe, be far more likely to survive than those with more traditional views.

What is much more difficult to predict is when the changes will occur. Some commentators seem to imply that the change is imminent and will be dramatic, but the pace of change depends on many factors. In order for such a scenario to happen a large majority of architects and designers would need to become active users of 3D modelling systems for the majority of their work. Whilst the most recent published survey (Peat, Marwick, McLintock 1987) shows that 62 per cent of architectural practices surveyed presently use CADD software with a further 16 per cent forecasting use in the future, indications are that the majority of these employ low cost 2D or 2.5D systems simply to cope with the draughting work. Such systems are in general quite unsuited to the generation of quantity data in a form necessary to invite competitive tenders. In addition 3D CAD systems are still very expensive, and both Wager and Wilson (1986) and Atkin (1987) report that even these systems cannot themselves generate quantity data in an acceptable form at the present time without the links to quantity surveying software reviewed earlier.

Whilst it is no doubt inevitable that the price of 3D CAD systems will fall, probably dramatically as new computing technologies such as parallel processing become widely available, and the problems posed by the conversion of graphical data into a form required for tendering will eventually be resolved, experience seems to show that the latent inertia of the construction industry will ensure that the widespread adoption of these techniques by the rank and file is likely to take a lengthy period of time. What is perhaps likely to happen in the long term (say within the next twenty years or so) as computer systems become more complex and the problems of data exchange between systems are resolved is a fundamental change in the tendering process itself to a stage where bills of quantities are no longer necessary. Nationally agreed methods of measurement are, after all, a compromise between what the contractor actually wants and what the quantity surveyor is prepared to provide; the bill gives tendering contractors little information about 'buildability' and yet the contractor's assessment of this factor is arguably the one thing upon which he needs to exercise his skill if his tender is to be successful and he is to gain an adequate return on his investment.

It is, for example, easy to imagine a scenario in which tendering contractors are each presented with a copy of the architect's CAD model in computer readable form. From such a model contractors could not only extract for themselves details of the quantities of work and materials required for the scheme but could also, in conjunction with their own management software, perform 'what-if' simulations in order to determine the most efficient and economical method of construction bearing in mind their own particular resource constraints.

A further factor which will influence the speed with which such changes come about is the economic state of the construction industry. As we have already seen, many of the earlier developments in CAD can be traced back to a period of intense constructional activity in which standardisation and computerisation became almost hallowed words. A significant increase in demand could well accelerate the process of change, and this factor is itself likely to be affected critically both by the possible influx of European companies following the removal of trade barriers in 1992 and also the increasing activity of foreign firms such as the major Japanese construction companies within the United Kingdom.

References

Atkin B. (1987) *CAD techniques: opportunities for chartered quantity surveyors* Royal Institution of Chartered Surveyors

Brandon P. (1983) 'The writing on the wall' *Chartered Quantity Surveyor* May 1983 pp. 378–379

Campion D. (1968) *Computers in architectural design* Elsevier

Carter J. (1973a-d) 'Computers and the architect' *The Architect's Journal* 3/10/73 pp. 815–817, 10/10/73 pp. 865–870, 24/10/73 pp. 1003–1011 and 31/10/73 pp. 1053–1060

CICA (1982) *The specification of a building industry computer workstation* Construction Industry Computing Association

Curran J. (1987) 'The quantity surveyor and the CAD system' *Chartered Quantity Surveyor* October 1987 p. 11

Daniel P. (1979) 'Bills of quantity in a multi-disciplined design system' *Chartered Quantity Surveyor* May 1979 pp. 141–142

Day A., Faulkner A. and Happold E. (1986) *Communications and computers in the building industry* Construction Industry Computing Association

Edgill B. and Atkin B. (1987) 'CAD opportunities for the quantity surveyor' *Chartered Quantity Surveyor* May 1987 p. 9

Hawkins M. and Davidson J. (1979) 'Computer aids Bills of Quantities' *Chartered Quantity Surveyor* April 1979 pp. 99–105

Jelly P. (1977) 'Project estimating by computer – a system in use' *The Quantity Surveyor* April 1977 pp. 161–165

Madden L.W. (1973) 'Computer programs for West Sussex' *Building* 4/5/73 pp. 103–107

Maver T. (1978) 'The benefits of using computer aided design' *RIBA Journal* March 1978 pp. 101–104

Peat, Marwick, McLintock (1987) *Building on IT* Peat, Marwick, McLintock Publications

RIB E.V. (1982) *Feasibility study of common I/O conventions for the building industry* Rechen-und Entwicklungsinstitut Fuer Edv im Bauswesen

Wager D. and Wilson R. (1986) *CAD systems and the quantity surveyor* Construction Industry Computing Association

Wix J. and McLelland C. (1986) *Data exchange between computer systems in the construction industry* Building Research and Information Association

13 Computers, Quantity Surveyors and Project Management

Objectives

At the end of this chapter you should be able to:
- Identify those parts of the project management process to which computers are most likely to be applied.
- Comment on the early history of computer based project management systems.
- Identify and comment on the features which a good project management system should possess.
- Discuss the advantages and disadvantages of modern microcomputer based project management software.
- Comment on the use of computer systems in the selection of an appropriate procurement methodology.
- Comment upon the possible uses of computers in quality control.

Introduction

Preceding chapters have considered the use of computers in 'traditional' quantity surveying activities, and it is perhaps appropriate that the book should end with a brief examination of the use of computers in project management since it is, in a sense, through the management function that all of the individual facets are united.

Quantity surveyors and project management

(Project management) is not for the faint hearted. The service attracts a high level of liability, needs an aggressive approach and will require quantity surveyors to open their doors to those who have not trained as Chartered Surveyors. With this service there is a tendency to become more commercial and less professional, especially if one moves towards the contracting end of the spectrum. Finally to achieve the rewards this

service can offer, one must be entrepreneurial, flexible and be prepared to take reasonable business risks.
(R. Morris, Hanscombe International Inc., Chicago; RICS Annual Conference 1986)

The increasing interest shown towards project management is no doubt based upon the perceived opportunities of a new market in which to apply quantity surveying skills. While this may be true in some cases, the offering of a complete management service involves more than just the repackaging of traditional quantity surveying. Managing complete projects requires specific skills which some quantity surveyors may not, as yet, possess.
(Brian Atkin, Lecturer in Construction Management, University of Reading; Chartered Quantity Surveyor September 1986.)

Despite comments such as those recorded above, increasing client dissatisfaction with traditional building procurement methods in the United Kingdom has led a number of quantity surveying practices to move away from the traditional role of measurer and valuer, and instead to assume the role of manager of the procurement process.

There have been notable successes; perhaps the best known is still the construction of the National Exhibition Centre in Birmingham, although others are reported from time to time.

Notwithstanding the fact that this form of procurement is no longer unusual, there still appears to be some confusion of terminology, with terms like 'project management', 'construction management' and 'project co-ordination' apparently being used almost synonymously. Project management is considered here to include the provision of all of the skills required to oversee the development process from inception to the hand-over of the completed building, whereas construction management is considered as that part of the total process concerned with the construction phase. Construction management can therefore be seen as one part of project management in its widest sense. Project management to most quantity surveyors implies the high level management and co-ordination of a project rather than the detailed management of the complexities of construction, and construction management is therefore likely to be done by a specialist under the control of the project manager.

The areas in which computer systems are likely to be most useful are therefore:

(i)   co-ordination of the design phase
(ii)   co-ordination and control of the construction phase
(iii) choice of a suitable contractual method
(iv)   quality control and checking procedures.

It must always be remembered however that although the computer may be used to aid the procurement process, effective management of any kind is not achievable by purely mechanistic means. No computer system can, for example, tell the project manager what to do about the consultant who persistently fails to meet his agreed programme dates or the contractor who, at every site meeting, promises that tomorrow he'll have more labour on site, and despite the fact that he's lost another three weeks in the last four week period he'll pull it all back eventually and finish on time. The computer can only help the project manager to evaluate the alternatives, to show what the consequences of a particular course of action are likely to be in terms of time and cost. Good project management software is no substitute for good management.

Project management techniques

Formalised project management techniques had their infancy in the 1950s, and were extensively developed in the United States during the Polaris programme of the late 50s and early 60s. The best known techniques were Critical Path Method (CPM) and the Programme Evaluation and Review Technique (PERT).

By 1960 these techniques were implemented on mainframe computers on both sides of the Atlantic, and their principal use was in the project based industries such as aerospace and construction. The techniques were intended to aid the control of time, cost and resources, and as is often the case were perceived by many in the construction industry to be a panacea for all ills. There was therefore considerable initial enthusiasm since the techniques apparently offered sophisticated methods of analysis applicable to many typical project management problems, for example the problem of time/cost trade-off.

As with so many early applications of computers, however, the early promise was not fulfilled and there was a disappointingly slow spread of the technique. The main reasons for this seem to have been:

(i)   Small and medium sized firms were unable to afford to purchase a computer of their own and hence used bureaux services. These were cumbersome, expensive and time consuming.

(ii)   The gradual realisation that computer software, no matter how clever, was no substitute for good management.

(iii)   The technique required substantial volumes of data to be input. Most firms did not have sufficiently detailed information about the behaviour of costs and their relationship with work methods.

(iv)   The systems were not user friendly, some required specialised staff and they tended to be remote from the managerial work-face.

Some, usually large, organisations who could afford to install in-house computers and who had sufficient information persevered with the technique, but the majority of companies either abandoned its use after a short time or never implemented the technique in the first place.

It was not, as with so many applications of computers, until low cost, powerful microcomputers became readily available at the beginning of the 1980s that a dramatic new groundswell of interest in project mamagement systems occurred, and this renewed interest coincided with the drive by clients for shorter development periods requiring much tighter planning and control than had been the case in the past.

Features of a good project management system

The characteristsics of a good project management system may be summarised as follows:

Simplicity

There seems to be a belief among academics and some management consultants that for any technique to be successful it must be complicated and only operable by highly qualified staff with deep specialist knowledge. Not only is this plainly untrue in project management it is arguably the most common cause of failure.

For any plan to work successfully it must be understood by everyone in the team, it must be communicated clearly and its authority must be unassailable.

Systematic

For any plan to succeed each activity must be considered systematically and its effect upon the project evaluated. The results of actions must then be measured against the plan to ensure that the plan is proceeding smoothly towards its objectives.

Flexibility

Many project plans fail because they are too rigid. Any plan must be dynamic and capable of rapid change to accommodate changes in circumstances. It is said that the only thing which is certain about any plan is that it will go wrong, so when it does management must be able to evaluate the effect of the problem and initiate the necessary corrective action.

Responsibility

Every member of the team must know precisely what his responsibilities are for the cumulative success of the total plan, and must be aware of the probable effects of failure to deliver.

In order that these characteristics may be effective the plan must include the following:

Objectives

A clear statement of objectives is needed before any project is begun. In most cases these will be the conditions expected to apply once the project is complete and will generally be expressed in terms of time, cost and quality.

A plan of action and a programme

The plan is simply a step-by-step statement of the action which has to be taken, by whom, when, at what cost and to what specification. A programme is simply a plan on a timescale.

A means of measuring performance

A plan is of no value unless it is capable of being monitored to ensure that it is moving smoothly towards the objective. To do this the plan must be designed so that 'milestones' are incorporated in order that reviews may take place at critical points. Criteria for measurement must be established at each milestone, again normally in terms of time, cost and quality.

The result of such measurement is normally a variance, and in this event the plan must be capable of being recast in order to place the project back on track.

A means of comparing achievement with initial objective

When the project has been completed it is necessary to compare what has been achieved with what was originally intended.

Software for co-ordination and planning

Operations research has provided several tools useful to project management, and those most often implemented in software of this kind are spreadsheets to show resource allocation, bar or Gantt charts and network analysis. All of these will normally be combined in a modern package.

At the heart of most systems is an algorithm for the calculation of the route through the network which links all of the most critical activities. This will normally show the quickest route to completion, and any overrun on a critical activity will cause an extension to the projected total project time. In practice of course this may not be strictly true since subsequent critical activities may be completed ahead of schedule and the lost time may therefore be regained.

In an effort to mitigate this problem some techniques, for example PERT, allow up to three durations to be set against each activity, namely an optimistic time, the most likely time and a pessimistic time. Planners can therefore explore probabilities, assess the effects of changes in more detail and make contingency plans in advance of problems actually occurring. Atkin (1986) contends that few commercial packages handle probabilities, but this is probably because few construction industry planners are sufficiently *au fait* with probability techniques to properly understand their use. Software suppliers assert that if such facilities were to be requested they could readily be made available.

Resources can also be assigned to activities. Often the duration of an activity implies a minimum resource usage derived from the work method. In other situations the duration is assigned regardless of work method. The resource pool available for a project can be stated and the resource forecast is calculated by aggregating the requirements and availability for each project time period. The result is often displayed as a histogram. Where the timescale requires a resource level higher than that available an overload occurs, and these will need to be eliminated by adjusting the plan, a process known as resource levelling. Many computer systems claim to offer resource levelling, but in reality only a few systems can achieve this to a satisfactory degree.

Once a project schedule is determined in terms of time and resources it can be stored and used to generate cost forecasts, resource requirement reports etc. for the use of the project team. This 'baseline' can then be used for comparison purposes as the work proceeds.

There is a very wide variety of packages available. Most will produce networks and Gantt charts; however some packages are network based and can handle extensive manipulations of networks, while some packages are Gantt based and can handle extensive manipulation of programme charts. The range of facilities offered with some of the newer medium priced packages may be greater, but for speed and capacity the larger packages are usually better. Some packages require 'bolt-on' graphics extensions, or may require their file contents to be exported to external databases or spreadsheets before display. The smaller packages are usually limited in facilities, although the facilities available do vary widely from one package to another. Many small packages are not aimed specifically at the construction industry and it will be necessary to take this into account when evaluating them in terms of value for money.

Some packages are now available which provide ready made 'templates' for the design stage of building projects, including standard networks and checklists covering concept, design development and tender documentation stages according to different contractual routes. Hunt (1987) describes such a system.

Costs may range from a few hundred pounds to several thousand, and generally the price band tends to reflect the facilities incorporated in the package. The low cost systems may have limited logic linkages, simple resource aggregation, elementary costing and limited activity handling. The more expensive packages are likely to offer several different types of logic linkage, resource levelling, multiple report formats and more sophisticated tracking, budgeting and costing features. A guide to the evaluation and selection of project management software is given in Barrett (1987).

In terms of hardware some of the smaller packages will run successfully on an IBM PC with one disk drive and a minimum of 512K RAM, whereas the more sophisticated packages are likely to require at least 640K RAM and 20MB hard disk.

A more detailed exposition of the use of computers in construction planning and control can be found in Jackson (1986).

Computer software designed to advise on procurement method

The choice of procurement method for any particular construction project will normally be made taking into account a number of factors concerning the client, the time available for the scheme, cost and the type of project. An incorrect choice is likely to lead to dissatisfaction on the part of the client either during the progress of the scheme or upon completion, and the problems will generally concern time, cost, quality or the degree of accountability, either individually or in combination. It is therefore important that the correct choice is made at the inception of the project, since if the choice of procurement method is grossly inappropriate the scheme is almost certainly doomed from the start no matter how good the subsequent project management.

Morledge (1987) develops an algorithm to guide the choice of an appropriate procurement methodology, implemented using a simple spreadsheet package, and an alternative approach to the same problem is proposed by Brandon, Basden, Hamilton and Stockley (1988).

Both systems attempt to attach value weightings to a wide range of factors under the general headings given above, and thus attempt to rank the most suitable procurement strategies.

Whilst in the majority of cases the most appropriate procurement strategy often appears fairly obvious, programs such as these can assist in clearly identifying those factors which are important in any particular scheme, particularly perhaps in the case of an inexperienced client whose true needs and priorities may not actually be those articulated in the project brief.

Software for quality control and checking

Whilst at present the construction industry makes little use of computer technology for this purpose, systems for quality control are in use in other industries.

A good example is the quality control system implemented by a leading car manufacturer in the final vehicle inspection area. This system consists of a small computer equipped with a voice synthesiser which prompts the vehicle inspector for each acceptance check required on a vehicle before it is allowed to leave the production line. The inspector is required to confirm to the computer that each check has been carried out and whether the item was satisfactory or not. Any unsatisfactory items are logged for subsequent attention.

One obvious use for such a system is in the final acceptance of building services installations or even complete buildings. At the moment many acceptance checks tend to be carried out on a fairly cursory basis, and the use of more structured methods might lead to both an improvement in building quality and a reduction in the number of dissatisfied clients.

References

Atkin B. (1986) 'Project planning and control' *Chartered Quantity Surveyor* September 1986 pp. 11–13

Barrett D. (1987) 'Head scratching stuff' *Computer Weekly* 24/9/87 p. 38

Brandon P.S., Basden A, Hamilton I., and Stockley J. (1988) *Expert systems: The strategic planning of construction projects* Royal Institution of Chartered Surveyors

Hunt G. (1987) 'The Tuxedo package' *Chartered Quantity Surveyor* June 1987 p. 13

Jackson M.J. (1986) *Computers in construction planning and control* Allen and Unwin

Morledge R. (1987) *Procurement management – Evaluation and development of choice methodology* M.Sc. Thesis, Heriot-Watt University

Index

Index